The Jungle Doctor Series No. 14

JUNGLE DOCTOR HUNTS BIG GAME

Books by Dr. Paul White
The JUNGLE DOCTOR Series

JUNGLE DOCTOR

JUNGLE DOCTOR ON SAFARI

JUNGLE DOCTOR OPERATES

JUNGLE DOCTOR ATTACKS
                    WITCHCRAFT

JUNGLE DOCTOR'S ENEMIES

JUNGLE DOCTOR MEETS A LION

JUNGLE DOCTOR TO THE RESCUE

JUNGLE DOCTOR'S CASE-BOOK

JUNGLE DOCTOR AND THE
                    WHIRLWIND

EYES ON JUNGLE DOCTOR

JUNGLE DOCTOR LOOKS FOR
                    TROUBLE

JUNGLE DOCTOR GOES WEST

JUNGLE DOCTOR STINGS A
                    SCORPION

JUNGLE DOCTOR HUNTS BIG GAME

JUNGLE DOCTOR ON THE HOP

JUNGLE DOCTOR'S CROOKED
                    DEALINGS

JUNGLE DOCTOR SPOTS A
                    LEOPARD

JUNGLE DOCTOR PULLS A LEG

DOCTOR OF TANGANYIKA
    How it all started

JUNGLE DOCTOR'S PROGRESS
    Brings the story up to date

JUNGLE DOCTOR PANORAMA
    A magnificent pictorial record

JUNGLE DOCTOR'S FABLES

JUNGLE DOCTOR'S MONKEY TALES

JUNGLE DOCTOR'S TUG-OF-WAR

JUNGLE DOCTOR'S HIPPO
                    HAPPENING

Jointly with Dr. David Britten:
THE RANFORD MYSTERY MILER

RUCTIONS AT RANFORD

RANFORD GOES FISHING

RANFORD IN FLAMES

PAUL WHITE

JUNGLE DOCTOR HUNTS BIG GAME

With Thirty-three Illustrations
by Graham Wade

THE PATERNOSTER PRESS

Copyright © 1956, The Paternoster Press

First Published	.	*September*, 1956
Second Impression	.	*April*, 1959
Third Impression	.	*March*, 1961
Fourth Impression	.	*September*, 1963
Fifth Impression	.	*September*, 1966

AUSTRALIA:
Emu Book Agencies Pty., Ltd.,
511, Kent Street, Sydney, N.S.W.

CANADA:
Home Evangel Books Ltd.,
25, Hobson Avenue, Toronto, 16

NEW ZEALAND:
G. W. Moore, Ltd.,
P.O. Box 29012 Greenwood's Corner,
24, Empire Road, Auckland

SOUTH AFRICA:
Oxford University Press
P.O. Box 1141
Thibault House, Thibault Street
Cape Town

Made and Printed in Great Britain for
The Paternoster Press, Paternoster House,
3 Mount Radford Crescent, Exeter, Devon
by Cox & Wyman, Limited
London, Fakenham and Reading

CONTENTS

CONTENTS

CHAPTER I

BAIT FOR THE TRAP

"Where's Mboga, Simba?"
The African hunter shrugged his shoulders. "*Magu*, Bwana, I don't know, but well before sunset he borrowed one of my goats."

"Borrowed a goat, eh? That's a strange thing; I saw him with a shovel over his shoulder walking down towards the river."

Simba jumped to his feet. "*Hongo*, Bwana, he's gone to set a trap! You know what he's like with traps! He loves 'em."

I nodded. "He's been catching bats in the baobab tree with strips of mosquito net and yesterday he had a bottle full of some horrible sticky mixture which he says takes the nimbleness from the legs of cockroaches."

Simba grinned. "Mboga's heard of the very large leopard that is raiding the cattle bomas by the sugar-cane gardens; perhaps he's working out one of his schemes down there."

"So he borrowed your goat, eh?"

"*Kah!* He wanted it for bait, Bwana—BAIT—my goat! *Punghati!*" Simba spat.

"It's the goat who is setting the trap that worries me, he . . ."

An excited voice interrupted me. "Bwana, Bwana, come quickly. Mboga has set a trap and caught trouble in it. Bwana, come quickly."

"What's he caught?"

"*Magu*, I don't know, but the growling would turn your blood to water."

Simba and I jumped into the truck. The hunter gripped his spear tensely.

We had travelled a mile when the air suddenly seemed full of the snarling of some animal, while there was a background

7

of excited voices. Simba lighted a hurricane lantern, fumbling in his eagerness. By its feeble light we saw Mboga and two stalwarts with spears poised, moving uneasily round a three-foot-wide hole.

Crouching in the background were quite a number of people, too thrilled to run away, too frightened to go close. A tangled mass of thornbush had been placed round the deep hole, while beyond it, straining at a stake, was Simba's goat.

Mboga rushed across to me.

"Bwana, quickly, bring a rifle, Chewi the leopard is in my trap."

"How deep is the hole?" demanded Simba.

Mboga's voice was high pitched with excitement. "Twice my height. It is shaped like a bottle. The women had used the place as a well. I dug it deeper. The top was covered with grass on thin sticks. Then I borrowed the goat and put it here and built a thornbush fence round it. The goat made much noise, and then the leopard came before I was ready for him and fell in."

"Did you put sharp stakes at the bottom of the trap?" Simba demanded.

Mboga shook his head.

Simba rolled his eyes. "At least you put a net inside that hole?"

"*Uh-huh*," Mboga shook his head. "Should there be a net?"

"*Kah!*" muttered Simba, drawing back, "this is great danger. If that leopard climbs out, he will kill many people."

He called to those who stood in the background. "*Upesi* —run! It is a situation of great danger; there is no profit in the caress of the teeth and claws of Chewi."

The night became full of fleeing shadows.

"Simba, we'll have to kill this brute somehow."

"How can you do it, Bwana? You can't even see down that hole. The edges are soft sand. Go too close, and *kumbe*, the sand will give way and you're with the leopard." He made dramatic clawing movements.

Even as he spoke, there was a heavy sound of falling sand, and the mouth of the animal trap yawned suddenly larger.

Simba held his spear poised for action. "*Kumbe*, the leopard will soon get out. There will be great trouble."

Mboga gripped a jungle knife. I thought quickly, and

then remembered that there was a length of hose and a bicycle tube in the tool-box of the old truck.

"Clear that thornbush out of the way," I ordered, "I want to drive backwards close to this hole."

"*Kah*," said Simba, "what for?"

"Clear the thornbush," I shouted, "no questions. Let's get on with it."

The hosing fitted into the bicycle tubing, which, when stretched, slipped firmly over the end of the exhaust pipe. Backing till the extensions of the exhaust would reach well down into the hole I put the brakes full on, left the engine running, and pushed the hose into the gaping darkness of the trap.

"Into the truck," I ordered, for the sand was continuously falling in.

We sat uneasily, listening to the regular running of the engine and the leopard raging in the pit. The snarling changed to a grunting cough, and then came silence.

"*Yoh*," yelled Simba, "it's out."

"Truly," I said quietly, "it's out."

Mboga grabbed my arm. "Then drive, Bwana, drive with speed, we're in great danger, *yoh*, even now it is waiting to spring."

"No," I said, getting out of the car, and switching the engine off. "It's out in another sense, it's unconscious and probably dead."

"*Koh!*" said Simba and Mboga together, closing the door and peering out with eyes full of fear. "It's dead? Who killed it?"

"I killed it."

"But you didn't, Bwana. You've only been sitting in the car."

"Nevertheless I killed it."

"But how, Bwana?"

Mboga shivered. "This is witchcraft."

I took the lantern and walked over to the trap. The goat bleated in terror. There was silence in the pit. Clutching their weapons, tensed for action, the two Africans were beside me.

I spoke. "No, it wasn't witchcraft. It was just plain poison gas. When the engine of old Sukuma here runs, it makes a very strong gas. We call it carbon monoxide.

Breathe that and it spoils your blood. This gas is strong, it is very poisonous indeed.''

Their eyes followed the makeshift tube which snaked down into the gloom. By holding the lantern on the blade of Simba's spear we could see a vague, limp shape slumped at the bottom. Mboga peered over and as he did so, the side

of the hole gave way. With a scream he disappeared. I caught up the hose.

"Hold your breath, Mboga, and grab the rubber hose and hold tightly, quickly," I shouted. "We'll pull you out, but hold tightly."

Simba's hands gripped below mine and we heaved.

Mboga's arm, then his head and shoulders, appeared. Simba threw himself flat and caught Mboga's wrist as his grip on the rubber slipped. With no little difficulty we dragged him urgently to safety.

He had been in the leopard trap only a matter of seconds, but he looked dazed, glassy-eyed.

"Bwana, the leopard's down there, it's . . ." He put his hand to his head. "I feel dizzy." He staggered and would have fallen.

"Of course you do; the hole is full of poison gas. It's more dangerous than a hundred leopards."

"*Kumbe!*" Simba whistled through his teeth, "leopards you can see, their teeth you can see, their claws you can see, but this gas, Bwana, *heeh*! It gives you the horrors!"

"Truly, it helps you to understand sin. You can't see it, it creeps on you, you can't smell it, but *kah*! it brings death."

"*Eeeeh!*" moaned Mboga, "my head, Bwana, my head."

"Breathe deeply with your hands cupped over your mouth and nose."

We watched as he followed out instructions. After a hundred breaths he yawned. "I'm feeling a bit better, Bwana, there is a small famine growing within me."

"Small famine!" laughed Simba as we bundled Mboga into the front seat, "surely you are on the path to recovery."

The headlights showed up the hospital gate as we swung past. "*Hongo*, Simba, may everyone here feel that way also. My holidays are due and I need 'em, with people like Mboga round the place."

"*Kwaheri*, Bwana. Good night," they called as I opened the door of our jungle house.

There was a pile of letters on the table. I looked at them rather wearily; my holiday was well overdue, and I was feeling the strain.

One letter slid off the table and landed at my feet. On the envelope was a small drawing of a charging rhinoceros. I tore it open with the sense of high adventure still with me and read:

"DEAR DOCTOR,
    Would you care to mix medicine and hunting for a month? I am *certain* you need a break—and my client is an enthusiastic photographer from Arizona who 'has a hunch we'll be needing a doctor'.

He looks unusually healthy and is amazingly well-equipped. Would appreciate your reply,

Yours,"

Then followed the signature of a famous big-game hunter, Colonel Johnson.   There was a P.S.

"This photographer seems to attract the oddest situations."

I folded the letter and quietly prayed that God would show me what was His wish in the matter.   Then I tore open a second letter.   It was a request to visit a hospital and district some four hundred miles away in a month's time, in the very centre of the best big-game district.

Here was my answer; everything fitted.

What a holiday—a safari that would produce payment, from which I could add considerably to our medical equipment, and a journey that would land me at the door of my destination.

CHAPTER II

INVITATION TO THE HUNT

THE leopard-skin was pegged out carefully in Simba's house. Mboga played his ilimba with two thoughtful thumbs, staring at the beautiful spotted skin.

"Bwana," he called, getting to his feet. "You understand about my bones."

I stopped in astonishment. "Your bones?"

"*Ndio*, yes, Bwana, they tell me that joy awaits me. My bones speak truly at most times."

"I hope so, Mboga; listen to this."

I read him the letter, then Simba appeared and it was re-read for his benefit.

"*Yoh*," said the hunter. "Now that is a matter of amazement." He rolled his eyes. "If only . . ."

"Mboga, you're coming on safari for at least six weeks; we shall travel to the Serengeti Plain." He looked at me dolefully.

"*Kah*, Bwana, that's the place full of animals, lion, and rhino, leopard, *heh*!" He rolled his eyes. "It is a place of danger, and *kumbe*, I am only Mboga, the vegetable. *Heh*, I have no desire to end up as food for wild animals."

"*Koh*," laughed Simba, "do lions eat spinach? Is it the custom of leopards to bring joy to their diet with vegetables? *Heh!*"

Mboga grinned. "You will need someone to look after you, Bwana."

"Truly, things happen on these safaris. With us will go one who is a great expert with *nhuti*, the rifle, and another who comes from the country of America, who takes photographs, *yoh*, ones that move. He desires to have pictures of lions and hippos and Twiga the giraffe and all the animals of the jungle. The closer he is to them the better his photographs and the greater his joy."

Mboga's eyes rolled again. "*Hongo*, it would be food for

the eyes to see these pictures! Perhaps I could trap something. I am good at making traps, Bwana."

"We've noticed that," I said heavily, looking down at the leopard-skin.

Simba moved from one foot to the other. "Bwana, do you think the Great One could have work for my spear?" His face was a picture of eagerness.

"Well, Simba, we can try but——"

He nodded. "You will speak the right words, Bwana."

That night the drums were beating in the Chief's village, cheerful drums with cheerful singing. The folk were celebrating the death of the leopard which had been stealing their cattle and bringing fear into the hearts of many.

In front of me was a large box and all over the place were all sorts of drugs and dressings and medicines that I might require. There was quinine for malaria, pills and injections for tropical dysentery, ampoules of specially prepared arsenic for sleeping-sickness, antibiotics, sulpha drugs—it was a regular pharmacy. There were surgical instruments, anæsthetics, and a portable sterilizer. It was a well-balanced emergency medical kit.

At nearly midnight I went to bed, climbing under the mosquito net. I looked carefully in the corners and then spent a busy minute finding and dealing with one of those same deadly insects, that weighed less than one of the hairs on Chewi's tail, but which was twice as dangerous as any leopard.

Next morning, most opportunely, Suliman the Indian trader arrived with his lorry. The staff turned out in force to say 'Kwaheri—good-bye' to Mboga, Simba and myself. The Indian supervised the loading of the boxes and bags that we needed for this big-game hunt.

We waved good-bye and the lorry swung down through the baobab grove, across the river flats and on through the tangle of thornbush jungle to Dodoma, the main town of Central Tanganyika.

The thornbush seemed to reach out across the rough, rocky road. Baboons scampered up on to granite boulders and chattered as we went past. Sharply the road swung downhill into a clearing. Suddenly Mboga was all excitement.

"Bwana, look! See, over there!" He pointed with his chin at a large bird the size of a turkey.

"It is *nhokwa nhokwa*. See, Bwana, it faces us; it is on our left-hand side. *Yoh*, this is a thing of great fortune."

"Tell me, what's all this about? Do you know anything about it, Suliman?"

The driver shook his head. "Indeed I do not."

Simba broke in. "Bwana, *nhokwa nhokwa* is a bird which gives you much help or much warning. When you see him looking towards you on your left, all will be well in your hunting; if you see him to the right, facing you, then go with care. If you see him in front of you, with his back to you, *koh*, it is a thing of danger. *Kumbe*, hunters have great joy when they see this great bird."

Suliman swung the vehicle hard to the right. I could see a great pile of granite boulders crowning a hill. Dodoma lay at its foot. Soon we had pulled up in the town itself and were bidding farewell to our Indian driver.

A letter awaited me, with instructions to be at the railway station at seven o'clock the next morning. I gave Mboga a list of things to buy in the town and watched him walk off jauntily with a peculiarly-shaped parcel under his arm. It was late afternoon when he returned with a satisfied look on his face.

"What of the markets, Mboga?"

"Bwana, I have done well. I have had words with the Indian and Arabs. None will give me the value of my leopard-skin, but old Hamise bought the python-skin for forty shillings."

My mind went back to another notable trap which resulted in a twelve-foot python losing its skin.

He held up a once white unbleached calico bag which held quite a collection of East African shillings. I looked up at him and smiled.

"You're fortunate to have a skin yourself, Mboga. If old

Chewi had got out of that very unsubstantial trap of yours. . . ."

I shrugged my shoulders. Mboga grinned.

The Tanganyika Railways were extremely active in the middle of the night. It seemed strange to hear the whistle of a locomotive and then, mixed up with it, the howl of a hyena that had been making the rounds of the dustbins of the town. The small birds were beginning their very early morning chatter when I heard Simba's voice at my door.

"*Hodi*, Bwana, *hodi*."

With him was Mboga, dressed in a brilliant red shirt.

"*Wera*, Bwana, it is dawning."

The small birds outside endorsed this statement.

"All is ready for our safari, Bwana, and I am about to cook breakfast."

He produced a very substantial one. As I dealt with his efforts, four African girls came and stood under one of the acacia trees. They pointed with their chins towards the house and giggled.

"*Honga*, Mboga, who are these?"

"Bwana, these are the daughters of my relations, Barinje. We have boxes to carry. Bwana, who better can carry boxes than women? To carry a box in your hands is a task of discomfort; to put a box the size of these on your shoulders is to invite blisters, but Bwana, to carry them on your head, *heh*, it is a thing of simplicity—for a woman."

The way one particular box with a big red cross on it was swung on to the smoothly shaved head of a slim lass sent shivers up my spine. In that box were the highly break-ables, a microscope, syringes and medicines that were essential for the health of the party on this safari. The girl balanced it for a moment and then walked confidently and briskly down the road towards the railway station where we were to meet Colonel Johnson and the photographer.

An African engine driver was again performing on the

whistle as we stopped before the double-storey whitewashed building which was roughly the half-way mark in the railway between the Indian Ocean and the Great Lakes.

Our loads were piled carefully in the shade when a jeep drew up. From behind the wheel stepped the hunter whose name was a by-word in the country for both his skill with a rifle and his knowledge of the animals that lived in such profusion in the great plains of Tanganyika.

He gripped my hand. "Good morning, Doctor. Got your stuff ready? Good! We have a jeep, a big three-tonner and a light truck with all the photographic stuff in it.

"I'll go ahead in this with the photographer Johnny—what a man he is! You've never seen so much equipment in all your born days. He's only one idea— pictures. We're going to have some fun and not a little excitement."

He smiled. "Hop in, and I'll drive you down to where the truck is and then you can come back and pick up your stuff."

The jeep swung away from the station and I left Mboga standing very carefully on guard.

"Have you many Africans with you by way of staff?" I asked.

"Fewer than usual. There is Kali, my gun-bearer, an invaluable chap. He seems to have a sixth sense with animals. And then there's Tembo, the cook."

He turned in through a cactus hedge. "There he is."

I looked at a little wizened man with a smile that seemed to be part of his face. Behind was a very smartly turned-out African with a little white cap that generally marks the Mohammedan. He was dressed in a carefully ironed white flowing garment called a *kanzu*.

"Wish I had a reliable spare driver; they're hard to come by."

"Maybe I could find one?"

The Colonel nodded. "Do."

We pulled up outside the door, where was a pile of photographic equipment, all tropic-proof packed. Standing over it was a tall American, dressed in the sort of cap that I always associate with baseball.

"May I introduce our joint responsibility, Mr. William Bailey?" smiled the Colonel.

He gripped my hand firmly. "Hi, Doc, glad to know you; it's swell to have a doctor on the safari, but hope you have nothing to do."

I agreed with this heartily.

"Did you see my personal attendant in the white night-shirt?"

"*Kanzu*, they call it," murmured the big-game hunter.

Bailey went on. "My, my, he's the whole caboose, laundry man, cleaning unit, housemaid, but he looks more than a little slick."

The Colonel smiled. "We'll keep an eye on him. Now let's pack everything."

He led me over to the three-ton lorry which contained much of the camping gear and the stores. There was just enough room for all our gear. I caught sight of Simba and winked.

"Colonel, there's a chap I can vouch for as a good driver and a useful man in a tight corner."

"Engage him as your relief driver, Doctor."

Simba's delighted grin saved me from the need to translate. The Colonel went on.

"We'll drive the jeep first, the half-tonner in the middle and you'll bring up the rear. I plan to camp on the other side of the tsetse fly belt—it's about 250 miles to the crater where we're going to set up our headquarters; we'll plan the campaign in detail there."

I nodded assent and was checking oil, water and tyres when I saw the long body of the American bending over the back of the truck groping in the tool-box.

"Carefully," I called, "you never know what . . ."

He straightened out like a piece of bent steel, leapt in the

the air, yelling, shaking his hand up and down. The safari hadn't started and here was our first casualty. I walked over to him.

"I'm bitten," he yelled, "say this *is* pain."

At that moment I saw Mboga with his convoy of African girls turning the corner of the hedge.

"The box with the medicines—quickly. The Bwana is bitten by *Nje* the Scorpion."

In a trice the medical box was open and a pain-relieving ointment was being rubbed into the tiny puncture of the bite.

"Up with your sleeve, Mr. Bailey, unless you like pain. You'll need morphia; they're fierce dudus, these scorpions."

As I removed the hypodermic needle and rubbed the spot, Simba appeared with a medium-sized scorpion held firmly in one of my best pairs of artery forceps.

"Say," said Bailey, "is that little fellow the cause of my trouble?"

Simba understood hardly a word but nodded his head and dropped the scorpion on the ground beside the photographer, whose heel made short work of the vicious creature.

For a while he rubbed his hand and then smiled. "That was fine. The pain's gone. Say, Doc, you're going to be quite useful on this safari."

CHAPTER III

SAFARI STARTS

Mboga and Simba sat beside me looking out through the windscreen of the three-ton lorry as we drove past the outskirts of the main Central Tanganyikan town of Dodoma. A long cloud of dust ahead was the jeep and the truck with all the photographic equipment. We brought up the rear of the safari rather sluggishly.

"Bwana," asked Mboga, as I twisted the wheel to dodge a particularly deep pothole. "Does this machine steer with joy?"

"It's heavy as an elephant and as nimble as a hippo."

Mboga laughed and produced his ilimba from a canvas bag. He twanged away happily on it as we drove. Dense thornbush was on each side for miles. We crossed a dry river and as we climbed the road wound through tall green timber.

Simba's deep voice came. "*Koh*, it's food for the eyes here." He pointed upwards. "Bwana, see!"

Seven great birds, complaining noisily, flew in a group overhead in peculiar flight.

"Hornbills," said Simba. "We call them '*chilimuwaa*'."

Another flight flew overhead, again screeching raucously, and the sound they made was very much like '*chilimuwaa*'.

Mboga grinned. "Bwana, see their bills. *Kah*, they are like the nose of that Ibrahimu, that very beautiful house-boy of the very tall Bwana, whom I call Bwana Kodaki."

I swung the heavy truck and pulled up beside the others, under a group of great umbrella-like trees. Preparations were well on the way towards morning tea. I went across to Bailey.

"How's the place where the scorpion bit you?"

He showed me his finger. "A little swollen, but no pain. That was good stuff you had, Doc."

I grinned. "I'm ready for anything in the way of insect

bites. Remember, out here, the biggest danger of all to us is not the big stuff that we're going to photograph, the lions, the rhino, the elephant, and all the rest of it; it's what the locals call the *dudus*, the insects, that do the damage."

The strip of leopard-skin on Colonel Johnson's wide-brimmed hat stood out sharply in a stray patch of sunlight as he nodded.

"That is exactly right, Doctor. Within the next hour, we are coming to a section of road that underlines that very thoroughly. It's tsetse fly country. A bite from one of those brutes makes you feel that you've been stabbed with a red-hot needle. They're so nimble that you're very fortunate even to hit one."

"What do they look like?"

"If you see a fly over half an inch long, with its wings crossed, that's a tsetse."

Bailey raised his eyebrows. "Sleeping-sickness?"

"Yes; not every fly carries it by any means, but every one can. There's a big campaign on round here to isolate them; the Government is bulldozing great three-mile clearings through the jungle. We'll come to a tsetse fly control point before long. You'll find that interesting."

Tea was made. Mboga served it and brought it round.

"Swell!" said the photographer, "cookies, eh?"

The Colonel said, "We're driving on through this tsetse fly belt and beyond it over a path that takes us into some real mountain country and then into the Great Plains. After that, we turn off at a place where you can see Mount Kilimanjaro. Think of it! Snow-capped right on the Equator, nineteen thousand feet up; it even tops the highest peak of the Rockies."

The cameraman nodded his head slowly, sipping his tea.

"We turn to the left, towards the Great Rift Wall, and come to a vast crater, a fantastic place, with everything you could possibly ask for in the way of animal life."

Bailey got to his feet. "Swell, swell. That's what I want."

"*Ndio*, Bwana, *tayari*—yes, sir, ready," came from the Africans.

In a moment we were on the Cape-to-Cairo Road again.

For two dusty hours we drove north. I pulled up sharply when the other vehicles loomed up in the dust cloud immediately ahead of us. Beside the road was a notice 'Tsetse Fly Control.' The track widened and doubled, one led through a big tin shed and the other was barred by the trunk of a tree held in two forks. This was raised and we moved into the tsetse fly area.

"*Punghati!*" Simba spat through the window in the direction of the tsetse Control Shed. "Have you roasted in one of those, Bwana?"

"No, but I will twenty miles farther on when we come out of this fly area."

Mboga rolled his eyes. "Truly, Bwana. The little things, the *dudus*, are the great danger of Tanganyika."

The road was red brown on a tan plain. Scattered thornbush was dotted here and there. Six ostrich ran away from the road down a little gully fringed by taller thorn trees. Four large giraffe stared at our convoy as we drove past. I smiled at the photographer leaning far out of the jeep, gesticulating.

"*Kah*," said Mboga, "Bwana Kodaki will have joy on this safari. The animals these days are moving closer to the water. There will be many about."

As if to bear out his words, a herd of zebra scampered away from the road, their tails swishing vigorously at the innumerable flies. They trotted sedately away from the road. Simba was counting loudly in Swahili.

"Forty, Bwana, *heeh*! there are many of them about, surely."

We climbed a quite steep hill and then the road came winding down to a patch of green, along a river now little more than a string of waterholes. Slowly we edged through the soft sand. A brilliant green and blue kingfisher darted amongst the trees, under which again the convoy came to a stop.

"Put stones in front of the wheels, Mboga," I ordered.

He leapt out. I saw his hand sweep round suddenly and

swat! There appeared to be a dead fly on his palm and then suddenly it whisked away.

Bailey, his cap at an angle, was adjusting a tripod and taking photographs of scores of the brilliantly-coloured butterflies that fluttered around.

I had pulled a branch off a tree and was using it as a fly-swish. The Colonel did likewise. He smiled.

"Our friend didn't take much notice of my warning about tsetse fly. This may be worth watching."

The whole of the photographer's interest was wrapped up in his camera. Its whirr stopped suddenly and he leapt in the air with a yell, his hands clapped to the back of his neck.

"My oh my!" he yelled.

"*Mbungo*, tsetse fly," said Kali, the gun-bearer, grinning widely.

Mboga covered his large mouth to smother his laughter. A split second later he too was caressing a tender spot. Tsetse fly bite is highly uncomfortable.

In a few seconds the vicious insects were swarming round.

"Back into the vehicles," ordered the Colonel, "and drive on."

"*Kah*," said Mboga, as he swished inside the cab of the truck with a branch he had torn from a tree. "Behold, Bwana, these *dudus* bite with strength."

"Truly, and they carry a very severe disease that can kill. Sleeping-sickness is a nasty thing, Spinach. You tell me at once if you find any swelling at the back of your neck."

Mboga caressed that portion of his anatomy with some care.

We drove on between low hills where soil erosion had creased the country with ugly ridges, and then on, over a sandy river-bed and up a stiff slope. At the top, the Colonel called a halt to pitch camp for the night. In the trees around us was a large collection of grey monkeys who watched us warily and discussed us with considerable chattering and yammering.

As darkness came on and hurricane lamps were lit, the jungle birds began to say their own particular good night. On the evening air came the rhythm of drums and singing.

Simba stood listening. "Those fellows surely come from our tribe. I know those songs, Bwana."

Mboga nodded. "Bwana, we will find amongst them some

people whom you have helped. Many come from this part of the country to our hospital."

"After food," I said, "we will go and greet them."

The wizened little cook, Tembo, had been extremely busy and a most interesting smell was coming from round his fireplace.

"Doc," came a voice, "how about some of that medicine of yours that takes the fire out of these bites—you're sure right when you call those tsetse's *dudus*, they certainly do do!"

From the medicine case came the necessary tube. I rubbed ointment gently over three angry red patches. "How's that, Mr. Bailey?"

"Better, Doc, but say, call me Bill, it saves time."

"Right, Bill it is."

He massaged one spot tenderly and looked up. "Say, what do these lads call me?"

"You've acquired a new name; Mboga called you Bwana Kodaki, and it's caught on."

"Good enough, Doc." He walked on for a while. "Say, tell me about these tsetse fly, what exactly is the score?"

"They're carriers of East Africa's pet disease, sleeping-sickness, a nasty sort of a set-up. Tsetse bite causes a strange-looking nightmare parasite called Trypnasome to appear in your blood. It looks like a sausage with a sail on it."

Bill screwed a filter on to a small camera. "How do you know you've got it?"

"A drop of blood under the microscope will show it up. The parasites gradually increase in your bloodstream. First of all, you find some swollen glands at the back of your neck, then some three weeks or so after the bite, you get feverish, headachy, seasick—just like an attack of the 'flu. Later come some thoroughly uncomfortable complications. But cheer up, a syringe, a needle and an ampoule of the right medicine and the trypnasome loses interest."

"You won't need to give me a shot, Doc. Mrs. Bailey's little Bill is disgustingly healthy, except that he sneezes better than anyone in Tucson, Arizona, if he meets sardines, timothy grass or horse dander."

"We're going down to the village this evening, Bill. Would you care to come along and try your nose on the local pollens and proteins?"

"Sure! Sure! And say, have these guys ever seen a movie?"

"It's very unlikely; actually I've got a portable film-projector and was going to show them a bit of an African version of 'Pilgrim's Progress'."

"Fine, let's show 'em a cartoon first, there's a dandy one full of mice and cats and bows and arrows and slapstick."

Mboga stood in the shade gently thumbing his ilimba. He and Bill had hardly a word in common but were obviously on good terms.

"What's that guy's name, Doc?"

He pointed with his chin at Mboga. The African gesture brought a delightful grin from the musician, whose thumbs produced a more enthusiastic melody.

"Mboga—or if you like it better translated, Spinach!"

Bill slapped his thigh. "Swell, play that bit over again, Spinach."

Mboga grasped the idea and produced music from his cigar-box and umbrella-spokes contrivance.

"Reminds me of my Grandma's musical-box, Doc. He's sure a melodious vegetable."

Mboga was playing the melody of a tribal folk song again, and Bill suddenly started to whistle an *obbligato* which twined itself most elegantly round the African theme.

The shining face of the minstrel acknowledged his art.

"*Yali fundi kabisa*, Bwana."

Bill cocked an eye inquiringly.

"He says you're a great expert."

Mboga burst into a spate of words. I translated.

"He says, 'Why not do this tonight when we visit the village; those that listen will have strong joy to have such food for their ears'."

The photographer chuckled. "That's a flowery mouthful. Tell him I think he's got a hot gadget and we make a swell item."

This I duly put into Chigogo.

"Ask him if he'd like to see a movie tonight."

Mboga's eyes opened wide and one word came—"Swell!"

We all laughed.

I told the Colonel about the idea.

He nodded. "It might be wise for Kali to go along with a rifle; there seem to be more leopard about than usual."

"That's so; a couple of days before the safari started, Mboga trapped one."

I told the story. Bailey's eyes gleamed. "What a picture *that* would have made!"

The big-game hunter smiled. "After all that, do you still feel like going with him?"

"Sure, he attracts action, does Doc!"

CHAPTER IV

PILGRIM'S PROGRESS

AFTER the evening meal, Mboga shouldered a battery that had been taken from the jeep. Simba clutched the portable projector which was my contribution to the night's entertainment.

Kali led the way, carrying a rifle. A powerful electric torch was pushed under his belt. The grass was tall and very damp with the evening dew. Ahead the camp-fires were red patches in the darkness.

Unexpectedly, above the sound of the crickets and surprisingly close, came the howl of a hyena.

"Oooh!" Bailey, who was never parted from one of his beloved cameras, swung the one he was carrying round ready for a flash-shot. "That was close."

Kali shook his head. "No, Bwana, the voice of the hyena is full of deception. It is many yards away."

The trees seemed to close in above us. The torch was switched off. It was suddenly solidly dark. Kali laughed.

"*Heh*, Bwana, this is the sort of place I like. Listen to the voice of the jungle."

The singing in the village had stopped, and as we walked on the night noises seemed to surround us; then without warning we were in a clearing. Figures were silhouetted against the firelight.

Africans leapt to their feet and someone let out the alarm cry, but I called out in their language.

"*Ali zosweru wenyu*—good evening!"

A group of men came slowly towards us.

"*Kah*," said one, "Bwana, we know you."

"*Eh-heh*," said Mboga, "and we know you. Is he not the Bwana from the hospital? Is he not the doctor?"

An old man advanced to greet me with both hands. "Bwana, we have joy to see you. *Kah*, did you not give me the

27

medicine that deals with the sickness that you call the sickness of sleep?"

I nodded and translated.

"Say," said Bill Bailey, "what did you feel, grandfather?"

Again I interpreted.

The old man turned slowly round and pointed to the back of his neck. "Here, lumps appeared. I had much headache and my skin had great itchiness."

"Say, were you bitten, grandfather, by that bug which flies like a jet-propelled aircraft?"

What a lovely sentence to translate, I thought, and asked the African in his own language: "He asks were you bitten by the *dudu* that flies with the speed of the honey-eater?"

The old man nodded. "I was and, behold, it is a *dudu* of great danger. It brings strong sickness. You must avoid being bitten by it. There are many of them in this country."

Suddenly, from the far side of the firelight came striding a tall figure with his hand outstretched.

"Bwana," he said, "it is joy for me to see you."

Mboga peered at him and I tried to see as much as I could in the flickering firelight. It would be hard to find a more cheerful, happy-looking individual.

"*Kumbe!*" I replied. "Your face brings joy to anyone's heart. *Kah*, surely when you were at the hospital, you took the medicine that comes out of no bottle."

The African laughed. "Bwana, that is true, I am Tadayo. I tasted medicine one day when I was going past Mvumi herding cattle. I had a cough in my throat, but within me, Bwana, was that worm called fear.

"There was one there, Yohanna, *kumbe*! he had a face smooth from smiling. He had peace inside.

"After he gave me medicine, he talked to me and said that for him, living had no fears and because of the Son of God, dying and death and afterwards were matters without dread.

"*Kumbe!* Bwana, my mouth was full of questions. Yohanna told me about Yesu Cristo, and how He drew out the fangs of sin. He talked about the Cross and the earthquake and the empty grave—many words of wonder.

"That started it, Bwana. There were those who taught us to read with great speed. *Heh*, I arrived in Dodoma on *alhamisi*, Thursday, and on *jumatatu*, Monday, I could read. Bwana, this book," he held up a New Testament which was extremely worn, "has made the difference, *koh*, and there is joy in my heart."

All this I carefully put into English for Bill's benefit. He shuffled his feet and looked uncomfortable.

The village folk had crowded round. Mboga turned to them. "We have words tangled in music that bring joy to the ear. Listen."

He pulled his ilimba from underneath his shirt and started to sing. Bill Bailey's whistling came in softly behind it. The people nodded their heads. As he sang, a hoarse whisper in Swahili came clearly.

"*Mzuri kabias*—very good."

Tadayo whispered in my ear. "The people of this village have no joy in the Words of God, Bwana, there is one here, a witchdoctor, whose hand is strong to bring fear."

"We have a thing of wonder with us, Tadayo, which will bring amazement to those who see and will perhaps weaken the witchdoctor's grip."

Mboga's thumbs were moving faster and producing a lively tune and Bill's whistling blended beautifully.

More and more faces appeared out of the darkness and feet started to tap out the rhythm. Bodies began to sway. Kali and Simba had the sheet stretched taut between two trees, and as he whistled Bill adjusted the projector.

Simba suddenly called out, "*Hongo*, O elders of this village, Bwana Kodaki, who makes music by blowing through his teeth, is a great expert who makes pictures that move. He will show you things of wonder."

I broke in, "Truly, we come to bring you laughter. You will see *panya* the rat (the nearest I could get to Micky Mouse) and *nyao* the cat."

There was a sudden gasp as brilliant light lit up the sheet. The picture was quickly focused. From all round came a variety of exclamations of amazement as three mice armed with bows and arrows advanced on a sleeping blue and yellow cat.

There was a paralysed silence as three arrows suddenly bristled from the nose of the cat, there was a sharp indrawing of breath as mice and cat appeared and disappeared with startling suddenness. Doors slammed shut, the cat saw stars, furniture, walls, roofs fell with uncanny regularity, squashing one or all actors in the drama.

C

Suddenly there came a chuckle; it swelled into a roar of laughter, laughter that kept up well after the film ran out.

"*Kanhyi, kanhyi*—more," yelled the people.

I threaded up the film of an African version of Pilgrim's Progress and, with Mboga giving a musical accompaniment, told the story of Pilgrim's journey. They listened wordlessly until Christian came to the Cross and the burden rolled from his back.

The listeners looked at one another and just walked away. Suddenly a drum started to beat with an evil rhythm. The listeners scurried off into the darkness and the village seemed deserted.

"Say, did you see 'em disappear, Doc?"

"Witchdoctor, Bill."

"Bwana," came Simba's voice out of the darkness, "there is a woman here."

A beam of light showed up the scared face of a girl. Her words came in a spate. "Bwana, is it true that there is no entry into God's Kingdom for those who carry a burden?"

She slipped a black cloth from her shoulders.

"Say, she's got a great tumour between her shoulder-blades—look!"

A long hand came out of the darkness, grasped the girl roughly by the shoulder and swung her into a hut. We caught one brief glimpse of a tall figure with red ochre head-dress and then, but for ourselves, the village was empty.

A hyena howled eerily.

"Nasty atmosphere, Bill!"

He nodded. "Say, Doc, shall we go and sock that big stiff and give the girl a break?"

"Wrong way, Bill. The locals say, 'Hurry, Hurry, has no blessing'. We'll hear more of this later on."

"Give me action, hot and strong," he shrugged, "but you ought to know your way around." A gleam came into his eye and he spoke out of the corner of his mouth.

"Say, Doc, look at Mboga."

My cheerful houseboy had a look on his face I'd never seen before.

As he turned away from the light, Tadayo's voice came quietly. "I shall explain to her, and with God's help do more than that."

"*Punghati!*" Simba kept chuckling to himself as we walked back towards camp through the warm darkness.

Suddenly Bill spoke. "Say, do you believe all that stuff about God and eternal life and the Cross—all of that?"

"Yes, I do."

"You swallow it all, do you?"

"No, I believe it, Bill."

"Oh, brother, we must talk about this later on. The whole thing sticks in my thinking apparatus."

CHAPTER V

RHINO

WE struck camp at dawn. A tall column of dust marked our safari as we drove on over the plain. The road passed through country that showed the spoor of that strangest of beasts, the bulldozer. Its work was evident by the trees, thornbush and undergrowth ruthlessly dragged up and tossed to one side.

As we came to this vast belt of clearing there was another "Tsetse Control" notice. Barring our passage was a long pole right across the road and beside it a large corrugated iron shed with open doors.

Two uniformed Africans stood at attention and ushered the Colonel's car into the dark depths of this windowless building. The doors shut with a clang. After about three minutes, the far end of the shed opened and the car drove off.

When our turn came, first a red-capped African searched carefully with a miniature mosquito net; he swooped triumphantly on a tsetse fly hiding in a dark corner. He nodded his head and we drove in; there was near darkness in that tsetse fly trap and it was as hot as an oven.

"*Kah*," gasped Mboga, "surely this is a stove to cook tsetse fly."

I was about to agree when there came the shoosh, shoosh, of an insecticide spray and a voice counting "one, two, three," in Swahili. Every place likely to have a tsetse fly was faithfully dealt with. The more likely places were given five squirts, some received two and others three.

Then a voice came, "*Bassi*—finished."

The doors swung open, we were dazzled with the sun's glare; it was noon, with the sun directly overhead, only a few miles south of the Equator.

Mboga picked up a dead tsetse fly from the floor and carefully put it into a bottle.

"No fly could live, Bwana, after that treatment; truly they have cleared great belts of the country."

"They don't mean these brutes to get any farther, believe me, Mboga; this one *dudu* does more damage in Tanganyika than we can possibly imagine."

The Colonel came striding towards me. "Doctor, Bailey's in trouble."

The cameraman was sitting amongst his gear looking more than uncomfortable.

"Those bites, Doc, say, they are itching like fire. Oh boy, did that cooking in the bug trap make them burn."

Great weals had appeared where the tsetse had bitten him. Gently he rubbed ointment into the swollen spots, muttering murderous threats to all *dudus* in general, and tsetse fly in particular.

Then he started to sneeze and went on and on. His nose ran and his eyes watered. The red patches spread all over his body. A sizeable injection of adrenalin controlled his trouble and an hour later we moved on.

We were soon passing herds of zebra and wildebeest; between two low, sweeping hills fourteen giraffe stood in a thicket of thornbush, their heads turned slowly towards us, but their great spotted bodies almost invisible, camouflaged in the patchwork of sunlight and shadow.

In a dip was a place green with overhanging thornbush. To climb up the steep rise, Colonel Johnson had slowed down and was moving up the far side of the hill in low gear. Suddenly came the ominous thumping of huge, galloping feet, and I saw a great rhinoceros, head down, charging towards his car.

The Colonel had seen it, too. The jeep leaped forward, skidding wildly. A ton weight of wild animal seemed certain to crash into its side. The whole drama was obscured by a cloud of dust, and then we saw the rhino endeavouring to pull up, and the jeep careering off down the road with the photographer's truck close behind it.

"*Kumbe*," gasped Mboga, "look, Bwana, *Kifaru* the rhino is turning to charge at us, at *us*!"

The infuriated creature was galloping towards us. To go on meant inevitable collision. On one side was a steep bank, rising twenty feet above the road, and on the other, dense thornbush scrub, and then, rolling plain dotted with an

occasional thorn-tree.   But the thundering rhinoceros hooves
were a mere fifty yards away, and there was only one thing
to do.   I swung the wheel over hard and the three tonner
plunged into the thornbush undergrowth and forged its way
through tall grass.

Mboga, peering through the dust, shouted, "Bwana, it's
following us.   It's cunning.   *Koh, heh*, my blood is turning
to water."

Simba's voice was tense.   "We can go faster than any
rhino, Bwana, if only the ground stays level, but if we get
into an antbear hole, or something like that, *yoh*!"   He
rolled his eyes and spat "*Punghati*" at the galloping creature.

The accelerator was hard on the floor.   I drove forward,
dodging the larger thornbushes.   We seemed to be out-
distancing that resolute monster that charged along in our
dust.   Useless information came into my mind.   I remembered reading somewhere that a rhino's horn can sometimes
be up to four feet long and is highly prized as a medicine.

"Look out, Bwana!" yelled Mboga.

Immediately ahead, in the tall grass, gaped a soil-erosion
scar.   He and I saw it at the same time, six feet deep and ten
feet wide.   I dragged the wheel over again, furiously.   The

car skidded precariously on two wheels and then righted and shot off at right angles.

Mboga yelled with glee.

"*Kumbe*, Bwana, *Kifaru* couldn't stop and he's fallen into the *ikolongo*—the creek."

Dodging a giant anthill and several trees, we bumped along our wheel track. Out of the tall grass erupted the rhino. This time he was gaining on us because of the downgrade. Less than a quarter of a mile ahead was the road, but the distance between the pounding hooves and ourselves was narrowing dangerously.

A short cut seemed worth the risk. We crashed into a young sapling. The lorry shuddered but plunged forward through a cloud of blinding dust. The engine roared as the tyres gripped the firm road again, and we drove over the creek and up to safety.

Mboga was tapping me urgently on the shoulder.

"Look, Bwana Kodaki has been working with strength."

On the top of the bank, bareheaded, crouched Bill Bailey enthusiastically filming the whole adventure. His camera followed the rhino, who had suddenly lost interest in the proceedings and was ambling off the way he had come.

Simba pointed with his chin to a spot where Colonel Johnson stood, his rifle to his shoulder.

"*Hongo*, there was no danger, the Bwana had us covered all the time. *Kumbe*, Mboga, your blood turned to water for no purpose."

I passed this remark on to the hunter who smiled grimly and made no comment.

A few minutes later, still bareheaded, the photographer joined us. He was all enthusiastic.

"What a sequence! I shot the whole thing, even a close-up of the rhino charging you as you burst through those trees on to the road."

"That's grand," smiled the Colonel. "but listen, Mr. Bailey, if you don't wear something substantial on your head you'll get sunstroke. Old Sol plays queer tricks up here near the Equator."

The camera expert laughed and said he would remember, but things were tolerably hot in Arizona as well.

Kali and Simba poured water into the radiators of the vehicles. Along the road that we would shortly travel stalked half a dozen ostrich with their tail feathers up. Seeing us, they took fright and ran at a speed which would easily have outdistanced the rhino.

We drove on, the browns and greys and reds of those plains dancing under the dazzling sunlight. We lunched under a tent fly which was the only shade for miles. I noticed Bill Bailey had little to eat, and after the meal he quietly asked me for some aspirin.

"Head aching?" I asked.

He nodded. "We've had quite a morning."

He swallowed the pills and stood peering towards the horizon.

"Say, Colonel, am I seeing things, because if I am that's a sizable mirage. . . ."

The leader of our safari spoke quietly. "No, that's no mirage, it's a great sheet of water called Lake Manyara; it spreads right down to the foot of the great rift wall. You can see it up there. We climb up a narrow path and our track goes just to the right of it. I hope we don't cross the path of one of those crazy whirlwinds."

A great column of heated air and swirling dust staggered drunkenly across the plain. It reached from the clouds to the ground. High overhead, with still wings, circled a flight of birds.

"Vultures, ugly brutes with ugly ways," said the Colonel. "We'll see more of them. We had better move on now."

It was unspeakably oppressive, and a couple of hours rest would have been more than welcome.

"We'll all be more comfortable under the shadow of the mountains," said the Colonel, as he stepped into his vehicle. "I'll pull up if there is anything worth photographing."

We had travelled for an hour and climbed a long hill when I saw his jeep come to a sudden stop. In a dimple in the hill was a regular family of giraffes.

"Twelve of them," said Simba, "and three smaller ones."

As the camera was being carried back to the car, I was concerned to see the expression on Bill's face.

"Doc," he muttered, "my mouth's dry. I can't see straight. My head's throbbing."

Then he lifted his hands in the air in frank disgust. "Well, of all the ——! I've never done that before. All those shots on an empty camera."

"No more driving for you this afternoon, that's certain."

The Colonel nodded. "Kali will take over and you had better lie down amongst your equipment. We just can't afford to have the one man in the team whose doing the work, ill."

Slowly the safari moved on, up the escarpment and over the rolling hills with the horizon a background of great mountains, each of them a crater. At last we pulled up at a log cabin perched on the edge of one of these great cauldrons. A notice told us that it was seven thousand feet above sealevel. A couple of thousand feet beneath us stretched out a sheet of water and above it, in layers, were blue hills.

Kali pointed these out to me. "Bwana," he said, "the large one over there is the cooking-pot."

Then he pointed with his chin. "Over there, Bwana, are many swamps, *hongo*, and Nhembo the elephant and many of his tribe come there from the Serengeti Plain. It is the custom of the Bwana Colonel to climb the hill with three trees upon it and to look round with his telescope. *Koh,* Bwana, this is a place for animals."

"Give me a hand, Simba; we must get Bwana Bailey to bed."

Ibrahim had a camp stretcher erected and our patient was soon at rest. His pulse was fast and thin. After a quarter of an hour's search under the microscope, his blood showed no sign of any tropical fever. I went over to him.

"No obvious malaria, Bill; it is almost certainly sunstroke. We're going to sponge you down."

He nodded. "Say, I've never had a headache like this one."

His skin was burningly hot and dry. I spoke to Mboga in the Chigogo dialect.

"If we can get him to sweat, Mboga, he'll be all right, but if he doesn't, *kah*, there'll be trouble."

The night breeze was cool. I slipped a thermometer between Bill's lips and waited. The reading this time had risen to 105°. Beads of perspiration started on his forehead.

"Say," came his muffled voice, "I'm starting to feel a bit better, and am I thirsty!"

"Drink for all you are worth," I ordered, loading a syringe. "I'm going to take no risks. This could easily be malaria, although there didn't seem to be any parasites in your blood.

Mboga, hold his arm; it's no easy matter to inject into a person who is shivering as hard as our Bwana Kodaki."

But the needle found its way in and by the time the moon rose our sunstroke patient was asleep and his temperature had dropped to 100 degrees.

"Mboga, stay here with him until the small clock with the voice that makes a small tinkle speaks. That will be the middle of the night. Then come and wake me. Call me also if anything strange happens, or if he asks for me."

The African nodded. "*Eh-heh,* I'll do that, Bwana. I'll look after him as they looked after me when I had pneumonia in hospital."

"Do that. Fluids whenever you can get him to drink, but never wake your patient up, Mboga, to give him the medicine, unless that is written in letters of red upon his sickness paper."

Mboga nodded. "That will be done, Bwana."

CHAPTER VI

RUMBLINGS

I TURNED in and lay on my camp stretcher, mosquito net
carefully tucked in, listening to the night noises. It was
all very peaceful and quiet.

Sleep came and then, suddenly, I was wide awake. A
shadow had fallen across the tent, a deep voice whispered.

"Bwana, my stomach rumbles and my interior has no joy."
Simba's face appeared at the flap of the tent.

"In the medicine-box, Simba, a green bottle of pills."

The broad-shouldered African struck a match. For a
moment he fumbled and then. "It's locked, Bwana."

"Truly, and the key is in the hut with Bwana Kodaki. I
don't want to disturb him."

There was a click and a chuckle.

"Lock's open, Bwana. I tickled its ribs with a small
piece of wire."

He struck another match.

"Green bottle, two pills, thank you, Bwana."

"Whatever you do, Simba, don't make a habit of operating
on people's padlocks. They might consider you as bad
company."

Simba chuckled. "Do not fear, Bwana; good night."

The night noises faded into sleep.

I felt a hand on my shoulder. "Bwana, Bwana, it is I,
Mboga. It is the middle of the night. He sleeps well."

Carefully I swung out of that precarious bed and dressed.
Inside the hut all was quiet. Bill Bailey's pulse was fast and
strong. Under his arm went the thermometer. There was
no doubt about the diagnosis now. This was heat stroke,
and probably would take two or three days to clear up.

I walked over to the window, in the brilliant moonlight.
The mercury showed 100 degrees. Relieved, I leant on the
window-sill and looked over the wide sweep of countryside.

The night was amazingly clear. The line of volcanoes

was dark against the sky. Away to the west lay the vast sheet of blue water, Lake Victoria.

My thoughts turned to Simba, and how on a night like this he had killed a lion with a spear. Then to Perisi, his wife, and their four children; they were a splendid family.

A stout fellow was Simba, solid, understanding and trust-worthy, especially trustworthy.

Something moved under the shadow of a thorn-tree. Idly I looked at it and felt my skin begin to prickle! Four large lions walked sedately not thirty yards away from me. A lioness stopped and sniffed, then all turned in our direction. From the sick man beside me came a grunt. The lion looked more intently. I stayed absolutely still, knowing how in-tensely curious lions are.

From the jungle behind came noises. The black-maned male shook his head and turned to make off. The three lionesses seemed reluctant to follow. The crickets went on unconcernedly. I gripped the only weapon handy—the weighty camera tripod—and waited for the next move.

It came from an odd quarter. From over my head came a blinding flash of light. My mouth was too dry to produce a sound. Happily, the second flash showed the rear view of four disappearing lions.

Bill was clutching the window-ledge. "What a shot!" he gasped, as his knees buckled.

I grabbed him.

"Hold the camera, Doc, the camera!"

Clutching it between his limp body and my own, I managed to reach the bed. He half grinned at me.

"Saw you looking out there as if you'd seen a ghost. Thought it might be a picture."

"Listen, Stupidity," I said, tucking him in firmly, "you're mighty sick; no more of these tricks."

One eye opened, a half-smile twisted a mouth which said, "O.K. Doc, O.K.!"

Taking no risks, I injected a sedative. It was 2 a.m. when his regular breathing indicated sleep.

Soon my head started to nod.

The whole place reverberated with a deep rumbling roar.

I stumbled to my feet, almost upsetting the table in the gloom. The luminous clock showed 5.30 a.m.

There were no crickets active. Dawn was not far over

the horizon. Again the lions roared. Bailey stirred and thrust out his arm. I took his pulse. It was regular and strong. He was definitely improving.

Dawn came, and with it a collection of enthusiastic small birds. The Colonel stepped out of his tent. I greeted him.

"How's our patient?"

"I think he'll be all right today, but I'm not going to let him out until round about four o'clock when the sun has lost its sting, and then only with an approved hat."

The big-game hunter nodded. "Good idea." He pointed to the ground. "We've had visitors during the night."

"Yes, I saw a pride of lions there, four of them."

He pointed out their footprints. "At least five. You had buck, too, and a rather nice kudu."

"Quite a place, this."

Simba was squatting under a baobab tree when he saw me finish breakfast. He came over to me.

"Bwana, I have a word to speak."

"*Eh-heh*, Simba, what is the news of your stomach?"

"*Mzuri kabisa*, very well, Bwana, the medicine has strength, but my words are concerning that girl with the tumour. I know her, Bwana; she comes from a village not far from my own. Her relations are bad people."

He turned his head sideways. "*Punghati!*" He spat in his characteristic way. In the explosive sound was a sense of deep content.

"*Heeeh*, the situation is, Bwana, she has this tumour between her shoulders. None of the young men of the village would look at her when it came to marriage. They say it is a mark of the displeasure of the ancestors. To have her for a wife would be very bad luck, an invitation to trouble."

He was looking down at his left foot. His extremely agile toes were playing with a small pebble, and I couldn't help but notice the loss of the last joint of his first toe. I remembered that he had told me it had been bitten off by the claws of a giant spider when he was a small boy.

His voice went on. "It was in the days of famine, two harvests ago. Her relations said she was a person of small value so they sold her to a Masai cattle trader for the price of half-a-dozen cattle. Truly she lives in great misery, Bwana; her life has less to it than one of these skinny cows. The man whom we saw beats her with strength because she is childless, as are all his other women." Simba shrugged his shoulders.

"She lives far away from her relations and friends, there are few that speak her home language; truly she is one to be pitied with strength."

"Can we do anything to help her?"

Simba squatted down and drew diagrams in the sand, a sure sign he had worked out a comprehensive plan. He rolled his eyes.

"Bwana, did you see Mboga look at her?"

I nodded, but before any more could be said, Kali arrived at the double. He stood at attention.

"Bwana Doctor, the words of my Great One are that Simba is to make a small safari with me to find where Nhembo the elephant and his relatives have their ways these days."

"May you travel in peace under the shadow of the Pleiades," I replied.

Two wide grins rewarded this special African farewell. Both said "*Kwaheri*, good-bye, Bwana," and set out, one with a rifle over his shoulder, the other carrying his spear.

Mboga stood beside me. "Bwana Kodaki sleeps."

I satisfied myself that this was so and then went to where Ibrahim was doing the morning's washing, pounding soap-suds through shirts with his fist, in a way that would produce maximum wear and tear. He stood to his feet.

"Bwana?"

"At *saa sita*, noon, make coffee for Bwana Bailey. Make it with care, for those of America are experts in the matter of coffee."

A faint smile was traced round the African's lips. "I shall make it with care, Bwana."

"Mboga will stay with him until you have finished your washing, then I want you to sit quietly and report to me if he wakes up."

"*Ndio*, Bwana; yes, sir."

The sun was directly overhead.

Heat came shimmering over the wide stretch of thorn-bush that lay immediately between us and the line of volcanos in the distance.

Ibrahim came quietly; "Bwana, the sick one has awakened and speaks many words that I cannot understand."

I went into the hut. "How are you feeling, Bill?"

"Oh, brother," came his muffled voice from under the mosquito net, "have I got a headache!"

"How about some coffee, then? They grow grand stuff up there," I pointed with my chin toward Kilimanjaro.

I shook down the thermometer, put it in his mouth and counted his pulse. His eyes searched my face as I checked the fine line of mercury.

"Well, temperature's down, pulse is regular, once we've got rid of that headache you'll be able to do things. For the first few days it's going to be early morning and late afternoon stuff."

I wrung out a towel in water and put it over his head. "Lie still and take things quietly for a bit."

Ibrahim arrived with the coffee, which he served with all the niceties.

Bill nodded approval. "He knows his way around, does Ibrahim. He's been sitting there for the last two hours like my Aunt Kate just watching. I like these guys. That goes for your Spinach, too.

"Say, Doc, did you see his face last night when he saw that poor wretched girl with the tumour? If ever old Dan Cupid took a pot shot, he did it last night." He grinned as he sipped the coffee.

"Now that's real coffee! What about some more?"

"Right, two pills as well."

He pushed the pills far back on his tongue and swallowed.

I watched him slip off to sleep again and whispered to Ibrahim that he was to stay on the spot until four o'clock, when more coffee would be consumed.

At that hour Colonel Johnson came in.

"Off to get a few ducks; how are you feeling, Bailey?"

"Fine, I'll be out there tomorrow with my camera."

The Colonel smiled and waved his hand. He was accompanied by Tembo, the bow-legged cook, who grinned delightedly.

"Say, Doc," came a voice from under the mosquito net, "do you play chess?"

"I do, but what about your headache?"

"Oh, I'm a bit dizzy, but . . ."

Two games later I was rather thankful that he was dizzy as I tried to extricate my king from a very nasty situation.

A voice came at the door. "*Hodi*, Bwana."

I turned round. "Come in, Simba."

"Bwana, we have been to the village that lies in the deep thornbush; beyond it is a lake, and is it a place for pictures? It will bring joy to Bwana Kodaki."

"What's he say?" said Bill.

I translated.

Simba went on. "Bwana, there I saw a bird with odd eyes and a beak that makes it look like a hippopotamus on wings. There is also a long pink bird with very thin legs, surely it is the bird relation of the giraffe."

When I put this into English, the photographer smiled. "Pelican, I suppose, and flamingos. Anything else there, Simba?"

The African nodded. "There is a special place where shallow water is overlooked by high rocks. Here there are elephants, elephants and elephants."

Then in an altered tone. "And Bwana, there is a village not far from this place of elephants, perhaps one hour's safari away. It is a place of disease and trouble and tsetse flies.

"In this village, Masai cattle dealer has many friends. They are the relatives of the hyena, those ones. *Hongo*, there is pity in my heart for the girl with the tumour, who is called Mzito, the burden.

"*Punghati!*" he spat in deep disgust through the doorway.

"Also there are Masai who are not true Masais. They come from the same group as those," Simba chose his words carefully, "who hold the girl with the tumour, Mzito."

*   *   *   *

We had roast duck for dinner that night. The Colonel carved it expertly and said: "Well, gentlemen, it seems that Kali has found an admirable spot for filming elephants."

Having said this, he was extremely quiet for the whole evening meal.

As Ibrahim was clearing up the dishes the hunter stood up and touched me on the shoulder. We walked together to a spot looking out over the wide stretch of plain. He cleared his throat.

"Doctor, I took that driver Simba at your recommendation. I think you ought to know that somebody has been rummaging round in my store."

"Simba's not a thief, Colonel. I have known him for two years and none of my stuff has ever taken legs."

"That may well be, but very often these folk would take nothing from their own master, but it's a different matter when it comes to somebody else. Have you ever noticed his feet?"

I nodded.

"You may be interested to know there are footprints in the dust of my tent which show a damaged left foot. Another thing, the big screwdriver from the kit in the three-tonner was used to try and force open a metal cash-box. I'm not making any accusations, but keep your eyes open and your money safely stowed away."

Late next afternoon, to see how the camera-man's head would stand up to action, we drove out over the roadless plain, the jeep dodging between thornbushes. It seemed to be an afternoon for giraffes; a score of them stood watching us from a distance, and then galloped in their own peculiar way through an umbrella-tree-fringed creek.

The cameras were placed so that the tall creatures made a long silhouette against the skyline with its great fleecy masses of cloud.

"My, oh my," said Bill, "giraffe are always a picture; how still they keep their heads, but the rest of them . . ." He shook his head and laughed.

We came across buck and gazelle of all sorts. Only once we stopped, and that was to photograph a secretary bird. On a little rise was a fox which stood alertly watching us and made no attempt to move.

"Not a solitary lion!—not a one," mused Bailey.

"That's how it goes," replied the Colonel. "One day you may see a pride of ten or fifteen lions, then they go hunting somewhere else and you don't get a sign of them.

D

"But remember, because we don't see them, it doesn't say that they don't see us. I've the feeling that they are here all right. A lion's a shy creature in the daytime, but at night he fears nothing."

We watched the sun go over the hill; darkness came quite suddenly and the headlights picked out a dramatic display of animal eyes. There was a slight bump as though the jeep had passed over a large loose stone. The Colonel pulled up abruptly, and walked back along the track with a large torch. We saw the circle of light suddenly pick out a small creature struggling in the tall grass beside the track.

The hunter picked it up gently and came back to us. In his arms was a teddy-bear-like lion cub; the jeep had run over its back. The little creature was making pitiable noises. Johnson slipped off his safari jacket and wrapped the small cub in it. He drove back to camp very fast.

As we climbed out of the jeep he said, "I hate a thing like that to happen. Do you think there is anything you can do for him in the surgical line?"

I examined the cub by the light of a pressure-lamp. The back was badly crushed and both the back legs were paralysed.

Colonel Johnson caressed the little creature's head. "See what you can do, Doctor."

We got the primus stove going and various surgical instruments were sterilized in a saucepan. Simba had an old felt hat with a hole in the top and a gay parrot feather stuck in one side.

"Simba, bring along your hat. I want it to give this little lion an anæsthetic. Better take the feather out of it, though."

He came back with the dilapidated headgear.

"Bwana, here it is, but the feather has gone already."

The Colonel glanced up at him as he took the hat and placed it firmly over the lion cub's head. I stuffed gauze into the hole in the crown, and poured chloroform drop by drop on to it. The little animal struggled for a moment and then relaxed.

With Bill Bailey's electric razor, which was complete with battery, the hair was shaved off its spine. As Bill watched this going on he smiled.

"I guess my folks will say it's a fishy story when I tell them that we used that razor to shave a lion."

He sat down toying with his camera and some flash bulbs. It was obvious that he was over the worst of the heatstroke. I scrubbed my hands in a cut-down gasolene tin, Simba was doing the same, while Mboga fussed around very importantly.

"You would almost think that Mboga of yours was a nurse," said the Colonel.

Kali was leaning forward watching. "*Koh*," he said, "Great One, this is a thing beyond understanding. Without fear you take your rifle to shoot a lion and now for this small one, you have anxiety as for a sick child."

I saw Johnson's eye catch that of his gun-bearer, and a twinkle of understanding passed between them.

He spoke rather slower than usual. "If animals have to be shot, I shoot the old ones, the males. I can't stand to see things suffer. The camera is a better hunting device than the rifle."

I looked up.

"Ready to start now, Kali. Stand on that box and hold the torch. Mboga, do the same thing on the other side. Focus on the spot where I'm working; there must be plenty of light."

The little lion was properly anæsthetized and I set to work. The Colonel's eyebrows lifted as he saw the expert way in which Simba assisted. Every moment or two there came a flash.

"I don't like doing this," came Bill's apologetic voice, "but they don't operate on lions in Arizona."

With the bent ends of tea-spoons, we drew the muscles aside. Soon the whole matter became clear. I put down the scalpel.

"Spinal cord has been severed."

Simba sighed and picked up the instruments and put them back into the saucepans, relighted the primus stove, then said, "Bwana, may I dig a hole to bury him, a hole so big that no hyena or vulture will give trouble."

Nodding, I picked up the chloroform bottle and poured a steady stream on to the gauze-filled hole in the hat.

"A few minutes of this," I muttered, "and the little chap will pass out quite painlessly."

The instruments were back in their case and everything was cleared up when Colonel Johnson came in and said quietly:

"That unusual feather that Simba had in his hat, remember it?"

I nodded.

"Well, I found it in my tent. There is a thief amongst us on this safari, and Simba's under suspicion."

His muscular figure moved off in the darkness. I stared out in the region of Lake Victoria Nyanza, deeply depressed. The lion cub had been a very attractive little fellow and I had been unutterably unable to help. Then my thoughts turned to Simba.

He and I had shared a score of adventures.

Simba called himself a Christian and behaved like one, but now everything pointed to his being a thief.

Following the noise of his hoe, I went across to where he was digging. He leant on the handle of the hoe.

"Bwana, this is a strange thing, the place where I was digging sounded hollow, and look . . ."

I shone a torch down a hole at least eight feet deep; apparently an old tree had died and the white ants had been active.

"Put a box full of stones over it, Simba, we don't really want anyone to fall into it at night; we must bury the lion cub somewhere else."

Then I put my hand on his shoulder. "Simba, what have you been up to these days?"

He looked at me and laughed. "Bwana, I have been hunting, my heart within me sings, *koh*, it is full of joy and happiness, especially when I think that these days I have no burden on my back."

My fingers tapped on his shoulder. "Simba, you're not just putting on a show for me, are you? Someone's been trying to prise open the Bwana Colonel's strong-box with a screwdriver out of our lorry. Worse than that—the feather out of your hat was found in his tent."

Simba stood suddenly to attention. "Bwana, I did not do it. Before I followed the ways of God I stole things often, but not these days, Bwana. I did not go into the Great One's tent, nor did I try to steal his money. The feather was lost from my hat two days ago. You trust me, don't you, Bwana?"

"Simba, do you realize that your footprints were in the Bwana Colonel's tent?"

I shone the torch light on his left foot. "Is there anyone else on this safari who has toes like yours?"

Simba shrugged his shoulders. "I didn't do it, Bwana." He started to dig in another spot.

Heavy-hearted, I went back to my tent.

CHAPTER VII

ANT-BEAR

IT was the most ghostly, moaning noise imaginable.

I sat up in bed wild-eyed; then there was silence. For some time I listened. Then there was a crash, horse-like snorting and considerable yelling.

The Colonel was out of his tent in a twinkling, rifle in hand. A shell clicked into the breech. Then came the boom of Kali's laughter.

"Great One, it is the beast with a tail at each end, and ears like *Punda* the donkey—the creature that digs holes in the middle of the road, and delights to eat white ants."

Bill appeared bare-footed with a camera poised for action. He did not realize that there were small burrs in abundance. I found it hard not to laugh when I saw him jumping into the air, clawing at his feet. Ibrahim arrived at the double, a pair of shoes in his hand.

Mboga was holding a powerful lantern above his head. I could see the spot where Simba had buried the lion cub, also the hole that he had first uncovered. Grunts and snorts came from the bottom of this.

We peered down to see an odd-looking beast. Kali's description was right; it had the ears of a donkey, apart from that fact it would have been quite difficult to tell which end was which.

"Ant-bear," came Johnson's voice, "otherwise called aardvark; never see them in the daytime."

"So I won't get a movie of an ant-bear," came Bill's disappointed voice.

He peered down the hole and the darkness was split by his flashlight.

"It's like taking a picture down a chimney," he grumbled. "I'll give ten dollars to the man who traps that creature for me."

In crisp Swahili, Colonel Johnson passed this on. Kali,

grinning, shook his head; the whole of his muscular frame seemed to shake as well.   I could see the broad smile on the professional hunter's face.

"What about Simba?" asked Bill.

We looked around, but Simba was not there.   Mboga broke in:

"I'll get it, I'm good at traps."

He came back with a long board from the back of the truck. It had strips of narrow wood nailed across it, ladder-like. In his hand were two corn-sacks.

"Great One," he said, "tell me, has this creature teeth?"

The Colonel shook his head.

"Has it joy to scratch with its claws?"

Again the negative.

Mboga put the board into the hole and scrambled down. Lights were focused on a most diverting scene.

The would-be-trapper advanced gingerly with his sack held wide open.   The stocky creature backed away.

Mboga circled like a gladiator.   Every few seconds the unusual stage was lit up brilliantly by the flash-bulb light.

"Bag it, Spinach," urged Bill.

Slowly Mboga drove the ant-bear into a corner.   Unexpectedly it rushed at him, the improvised ladder slipped farther into the hole and the ant-bear made a dash up it.   Bill thrust his camera at me and grabbed the second sack.

"Quick, catch it, catch it," he yelled.

The odd-looking creature turned suddenly, nose over tail, the cameraman threw his arms around it, and then as if he had touched a live wire, went flat on his back.   The ant-bear disappeared into the darkness.

Bill lay there, a startled expression on his face.   His fall had been accompanied by the sound of tearing cloth.   His hand went round to investigate the damage.

"Say," he grinned, "my end is in sight."

The night was full of laughter, and then came a plaintive voice from down the hole.

"There is small joy to be beneath the surface of the earth."

"*Hongo*," said Kali, "did you not know that holes like that are the homes of centipedes and other *dudus* of ferocity?"

A minute later Mboga was on the surface and he and Bill were saying consoling things to one another.

Neither understood a single word that the other was

saying, but they seemed to find strange comfort in the conversation.

Colonel Johnson and I stood chuckling outside my tent when a torchlight swung down the path and Bill appeared, panting.

"Say, Johnson, someone's been at my stuff, they've forced the lock of my grip and walked off with a bag full of East African shillings and notes."

"How much have you lost, Bailey?"

"Only about fifty dollars worth, it could be a lot worse."

The Colonel nodded. "The point is, someone is a thief; where is that Simba fellow?"

"I didn't see him in the ant-bear incident and that's the sort of thing he'd revel in. Leave this to me, I'll deal with it in the morning."

At dawn Mboga appeared with a cup of tea.

"Thanks, Vegetable. Good morning to you."

"It is not a good morning, Bwana, there is a sorrow in my heart so great that my stomach ceases to have joy in food."

"What's up?"

"Simba has gone, completely, Bwana."

"It looks bad, Mboga, with that money stolen."

Mboga nodded, his face full of misery.

"Also, Bwana, with his help, much would have been possible for Mzito, but now . . ."

He shrugged his shoulders.

CHAPTER VIII

RABBIT PUNCH

To me it was a day to relax.

Mboga squatted in the doorway, a picture of misery; he thumbed his ilimba and chanted an entirely doleful melody.

Bill Bailey sat, his head wrapped in a wet towel, whistling softly a very harmonious *obbligato*.

Mboga's mouth softened and he played dreamily, Bailey's eyes were shut, his lips producing some quite surprising music.

Suddenly the African put down his musical box, smiled all over his face and said: "Swell."

Bill slowly unwound the towel.

"Say, Doc, if only I had a trombone!

"You know, that's how the 'Blues' were born. Hasn't that Vegetable got some tunes, wow!"

"There's very real melody in his stuff, but does your head feel like music?"

"It's lots better, Doc. I've been drawing up a schedule of the things that I want to see and photograph. I want shots of lions, especially little ones; also a lion hunting, and if I can, a new slant, something that other people haven't got yet."

He spoke jerkily as he made notes.

"Then I want elephants, not just elephants, but the great creatures playing round, doing things. Boy, have we gotten a slant on rhino! And then I want giraffe—I specially like the little ones. I want a sequence on hyena too—How I hate 'em!—and leopards doing things. Then I want some bird shots."

The Colonel came in and looked over the schedule which had been drawn up.

He nodded. "We can start with that elephant idea tomorrow. It will mean a dawn safari. We will take the jeep to within three miles of the spot that Kali has located; he says it's a great rock most strategically placed near a shallow lake where the elephants love to wallow in the mud. We may need to sleep there so we'll take a fair bit of kit."

Half an hour before dawn next day, Bill was awake and active.

"Doc," he said, as he got his cameras ready, "not a clue left to show I ever had a headache—I'm fit for anything."

When there was enough visibility to drive, Colonel Johnson got behind the wheel of the jeep, which had been parked under the great limbs of a giant baobab tree. It was very fully loaded. Kali was in the back surrounded by baggage, a rifle across his knee. I sat between the driver and Bill who had one camera round his neck, another in his hand, while the tripod and other equipment was organized for instant action.

Mboga and Ibrahim were going on foot. The Swahili houseboy was very much the gentleman's gentleman. He wore a little white cap, a long flowing kanzu and carried an ornate walking-stick. Mboga was dressed in a pair of khaki shorts. A bulky package tied up in red cotton material was over his shoulder, and under his arm was an enormous paw-paw.

The sun was coming up behind the mountain.

"That's colour," said Bill, "and look at the decorative effect of those trees on the skyline."

The jeep came to a stop and he took a number of shots. The Colonel pointed high in the air.

"See the vultures circling a thousand feet up? There's something down on the plain we must have a look at."

The squat little vehicle rolled almost silently down the slope. We stopped with a jerk.

The big-game hunter moved towards a shallow creek about three feet wide and four feet deep. Bent double we followed him, our feet soundless in the sand.

A great boulder swung the dry watercourse into a sharp bend. Johnson stopped, then slowly moved round the mass of granite.

His fingers moved back the safety catch of his rifle. He crouched again and we followed. Kali was within a foot of me with the cameras, and Bill was behind him muttering, "Let's go, let's go!"

Our leader stopped and motioned for us to look over the crumbling edge of the bank.

Not twenty feet away was a large black-maned lion standing beside a Grant's gazelle, his kill of the night before.

Bill was thoroughly on the job. The tripod was in position, and I wondered how the noise of the camera could possibly not arouse the great beast's curiosity.

Kali gripped my arm and pointed upward with his chin, following the gaze of the lion. In the air, coming lower all the time were vultures and great maribou storks. The lion walked round his kill irritably, grunting deep threats.

I found it very comforting to see Colonel Johnson's rifle pointing steadily towards the shoulder of the great animal. I could feel my heart moving into my throat as the large head turned in our direction, then it looked upward again at the circling scavengers. The lion roared in defiance and warning and moved away slowly down the creek towards a water-hole.

At once the vultures came in to land and shuffled round, squawking and moving awkwardly as they tore meat from the dead gazelle.

Bill's eyes were gleaming and he muttered away to himself as he slowly panned the camera. Kali was pointing with his chin again, and I saw a movement behind a clump of thorn bush. Apparently attracted by the vultures, from behind it there came a very large spotted hyena. He pushed his way through the noisy, ungainly birds and proceeded to gorge.

Bill had placed two big flat stones one on top of the other. From this vantage point he was squinting down the viewfinder. His finger again pressed the button and the camera whirred very quietly.

Colonel Johnson's voice came. "Look down to the left, beyond the ant-hill."

Very close to the ground, coming closer with hardly a sign of movement, was the lion. He skirted some bushes and then with a grunting roar sprang in amongst the scavengers. There was a vast fluttering and a cloud of feathers seemed to fly in every direction, the lion striking heavily with both paws. The din those huge birds made was deafening.

"Watch that lion," came Colonel Johnson's quiet voice.

Its muscles tensed, and then suddenly the great cat leapt high in the air to drag down a vulture who had circled too low. Its horrible squawking stopped suddenly. The lion stood there, his tail moving majestically, looking with infinite disdain at the ugly birds that circled overhead, and slowly made off. He grasped his kill and dragged it off into the thornbush.

Bill was hastily reloading his camera. "Boy, oh boy, did you see that? Did you see the cat cope with that sparrow?"

The Colonel spoke quietly. "In a moment you will be able to photograph the whole battlefield, not only the sparrows, as you call them, but an outsize in hyenas."

Bailey's eyebrows arched into a question mark. We climbed out of the creek. The grass was heavily trampled and the whole area looked like a slaughter-house. The dead vulture was grotesque with its broken neck. The Colonel's rifle pointed beyond the dead bird and Bill's eyes opened wide when he saw the huge hyena stone dead, its neck, too, tilted at a very odd angle.

"Say," he said, taking a reading with his light-meter, "so that's the rabbit punch, is it?"

He was busy for some time taking pictures.

Unobtrusively the hunter kept in the background, his rifle at the ready.

Bill was bubbling over with enthusiasm. "Oh, brother, what a box full of pictures that was!"

We bundled back into the jeep and drove on.

"Where's this elephant park, Colonel?"

"Round the next hill you'll see a sort of a cliff above the lake. That will be our camping place for the next two or three days. We'll . . ."

Kali's voice, unusually high-pitched, to indicate distance, interrupted. "*Kule*—over there, Bwana."

He pointed with his chin.

The Colonel slowed down and reached for his rifle and fired.

Kali leapt through the grass.

"I saw nothing," said Bill.

"Nor did I. What was it, Colonel?"

"If you men like turkey, you are in for a feast," smiled the driver as Kali came up carrying a large bird.

"Bustard, they call it."

Bill's eyes gleamed. "If there is one thing that Mrs. Bailey's son knows how to cook, it's turkey; I'll not let that Mboga ruin a meal like this one promises to be. He lets too much of his sense of humour get into his cookery and not enough of his music."

He kept us laughing with a series of stories of famous Thanksgiving Dinners.

The only possible track went round the hill to low-lying swampy ground. The jeep was being driven with great caution, but suddenly all four wheels spun futilely and the sturdy little vehicle settled down to her axles in mud.

"Swell," said Bill, "I wanted a picture of this."

The corners of the driver's mouth twisted a little. Kali produced spades and hoe. Bill sank ankle deep in mud but whistled happily through his teeth as he got the camera into position. Kali and I heaved for all we were worth, the jeep rocked.

Suddenly and unexpectedly the wheels gripped. I slipped and fell on my back in the soft ooze and a flying mass of soft mud caught me on the side of the face. A score of white egret flew into the air at the noise of unrestrained Arizona laughter.

"Doc, oh Doc," roared Bill, "and to think that I shot every bit of it! What a picture!"

The mud had a foul musty smell and I was a pretty sight. I rolled up a handful of the stuff and threw it at the grinning photographer. He dodged it easily and said:

"Say, Doc, I hope there's a bathroom at this hotel we are staying at tonight."

The mud dried quickly as we manhandled the jeep up the steep slope of a great outcrop of granite, using strong rope and an attachment to the front axle. The jeep climbed at a crazy angle; another hundred yards and the safari was over.

Trees overhung the edge of the rock. Beneath us was an ideal spot for photographing the stretch of swamp and water that lay fifty feet below. Everything was visible, and yet we ourselves were out of the line of vision, and, more important still, very considerably out of range of the noses of the animals we had come to photograph.

Bill was sitting on a large rock with a moist towel round his head.

"How are you feeling?"

"So-so, Doc. What a morning!"

I pointed down below with my chin. "How would you like that job?"

Kali, dressed only in a loincloth, had a bulging corn-sack over his shoulder.

"What's he doing?"

"We crossed the paths that the elephants normally come along. They wouldn't see our tracks but they would smell us. Kali has rubbed his legs and feet with elephant dung; he has a bag full of it over his shoulder. He will distribute that all over our tracks. It ought to obliterate everything, it's a pretty useful dodge.'"

Bill screwed up his nose.

I was taking a bath with a bucket of water and a tea-cup. Dressed in a clean shirt and shorts, I was feeling reasonably presentable when Mboga and Ibrahim arrived.

Mboga came across. "Bwana, ten minutes' safari behind us is a track that leads to a village. It is a place where the people have suspicion of Europeans. As we travelled I met one who told me that in this village they have special knowledge of a place 'ha-ndege', the place of birds. Yoh, Bwana, this will bring joy to the camera of Bwana Kodaki."

He went on at length and I nodded.

When the camp had been set up, Bill squatted on a camp-stool watching the cooking, over a primus stove, of what he called fried turkey. The Colonel would allow no open fires; he was taking no risks with the keen sense of smell of elephants.

We sat down to a delicious meal and I told of Mboga's story of the place of birds. The big-game hunter nodded.

"I've heard of this place; it's almost mythical, but believe me, Doctor, we must win the goodwill of the chief of this place or come across some strong magic or other if we are going to find this spot."

"It might be worth paying the chief a visit."

"I think it would. By the way, we must watch out for mosquitoes here; there should be millions of them coming up after nightfall."

Bill had his cameras all within reach and we stretched out in the shade in the heat of the afternoon.

I was more than half asleep. A crisp voice snapped me into complete wakefulness.

"Bailey, stand by, a brace of rhino."

A quarter of a mile away under a group of thorn-trees were two rhinoceros quietly standing looking at each other.

For two hours they stood there without moving a yard; the heat was intense, the wind blew in our faces. With the glasses I inspected the great beasts and the tick birds that strolled up their spines.

Graham Wade

Colonel Johnson's voice came quietly: "This is the mating season. In rhino courting the lady generally takes the initiative. Before long we should see some action."

Bill had three cameras ready, each with telephoto lenses in place.

The shadows were patterning the plain when the female turned and seemed to be talking persuasively.

The male seemed to shrug his shoulders, and turned side on. He made a striking silhouette against the billowy clouds on the horizon.

Bill almost purred. "Look at that background, it's perfect."

At the rhino end of things the lady was having no easy time, for the male lumbered off in a petulant way. She went purposefully after him.

Bill was whistling softly as he recorded every move on film.

The female suddenly lowered her head and seemed about to use her horn to some purpose, but her move was noted and, with a variety of snorts, both creatures stood nose to nose, heads moving up and down most hostilely.

Without warning, the male broke away and with an earth-shaking noise they galloped straight towards us.

Not fifty yards away they stopped dead and appeared to be muttering sweet rhino nothings into their absurdly small ears.

"Come on," whispered Bill, "tell her that she's cute."

E

As though obeying orders they turned and made quite a play with their dangerous-looking noses.

"That's a novel bit of necking," grinned Bill, "what else do you know?"

Both animals turned and the camera had before it two great rhino rumps with small tails wagging in apparent unison.

The Colonel sat back and laughed.

"That's what they think of you, Bailey."

Bill was enthusiastic. "That's wonderful, just tops. Oh, brother, what a sequence! I'll call it Rhino Romance!"

CHAPTER IX

ANTS

A LARGE variety of insects hovered around the lamp, while Colonel Johnson was spinning us yarns of previous hunting safaris.

"Somewhere in this region," he said, "is a mysterious small lake. You can pick it out from the air, but actually to get to it seems very difficult indeed. The local Africans feel that it is a place of spirits and they won't go near it, but there are fabulous stories of the bird life there."

Bill thumped the table with his fist and the insects swung away from the lamp. "That's the sort of thing I'm after. There are thousands of good pictures of this Noah's Ark, the animals walking round two by two or fifty by fifty, but I want them doing things, the sort of things that come into their everyday life."

The Colonel smiled. "If we could get away to this 'place of birds,' you certainly would find some shots like that. The only person likely to talk the locals into showing you the way to the place is the Doctor here, and he'd have to turn on some mighty powerful medicine to do that."

Bill turned to me. "Go to it, Doc."

"That's all very well, but how am I going to turn on medicine unless the people want something done. You see . . ."

Kali came running to the edge of the circle of light.

"Bwana!"

"Yes, Kali?" said the Colonel.

"Messengers have come from the village that lies to the west."

Kali pointed in that direction with his chin. "They request that the Bwana Doctor should go at once, they say a child is being eaten alive."

Eerily on the night air came the African alarm signal, high pitched, vibrating with fear. Mboga came running

63

with the medical bag in one hand and a hurricane lantern in the other. I picked up a large-sized electric torch.

One of the messengers was in a high state of nerves.

"Bwana, it is ants, quickly!"

At a steady trot we went down the path which led through the swamp, through thornbush, through dense overhanging jungle. It was unspeakably eerie. For some two miles we ran or struggled through mud or tall grass. At last the path broadened, gaunt limbs of baobab trees stretched overhead. Ahead loomed the village; a crowd of muttering people stood back as we arrived.

On the ground lay a twelve-year-old boy screaming. The ground all round him was saturated with hot water in which squirmed masses of red ants. Squatting beside him were two men trying to drag the insects from his quivering body, but they succeeded only in wrenching off the body while the head agonizingly gripped the child's skin like a minute vice.

Mboga's eyebrows were raised in question.

"*Kitanda*, Bwana?"

I nodded.

He ran through the crowd and came back a moment later carrying an African bed with criss-crossed rope in place of a mattress.

Gently I lifted the boy on to the bed and covered him with a blanket. He was profoundly shocked.

A stiff dose of morphia dulled his pain. His screaming changed to a continuous whimper.

Suddenly I felt a burning sensation in my leg; the pain of it blossomed into agony. The ground was still swarming with ants and many of them were climbing over my boots.

"Carry the bed into a hut," I ordered, stamping the ants from my feet.

I dragged up the leg of my trousers and wrenched the body off the three-quarter-inch insect whose jaws were locked in the tender skin of my thigh. The creature's jaws had to be prised open with a pair of forceps before the acute pain was relieved. The pain from one bite was severe, but the child had over three hundred heads in his body.

Shock was the first thing we had to fight to save his life. Fluid had to be forced into his system. The best way was into a vein, but the water that the people brought me was the colour of tomato soup.

I started to issue instructions. "A primus stove, a kettle,
china cups: I must distil this stuff."

Mboga said, "Bwana, it is already being done."

In the corner of the hut there was a dilapidated kettle, a
cup over its spout and still another cup beneath it. This
acted as a crude condenser. The second cup caught the
drops of clear distilled water.

Vaguely I wondered how Mboga knew about this; I had
never taught him. He brought a tray full of instruments
all newly sterilized and set up in a way which was exactly
that of our routine in the hospital.

A second primus stove came into action and I saw a broad-
shouldered figure bending over it.

The morphia was having its effect, and although the child
was relaxing, his pulse was still beating at an uncountable
speed.

Forceps made things easier and ant-heads were coming off
at a very satisfactory speed. I thought to myself, "If only
we had the hospital people here, how much could be done;
hot water bottles, or at least hot stones wrapped in blankets,
would help greatly."

Mboga was at my shoulder. "Bwana, I have brought a
big flat stone that has been heated in the fire, it has been
wrapped very carefully."

I put my arm against it. "Right, put it beside him."

"There are two others, Bwana."

"*Hongo*, Mboga, you're doing very well tonight; how
do you know all these medical things? You must have taken
in more at the hospital than I thought."

All the misery had gone out of his face and there was an
impish gleam in his eye. He went back to the primus stove
and I was amazed to see everything set up for an intravenous
injection. I broke open a small bottle and put its contents
into half a pint of water that we had distilled. A moment
later, the life-saving solution was running into the child's
veins.

A girl with a black cloth over her head and what looked
like a baby on her back stood beside me.

"Here," I said, "hold the boy's arm so that he does not
move."

She did so.

At one side of the hut were a group of people, wide-eyed,

watching everything. Suddenly some of them were thrust aside and a Masai warrior with red mud in his hair struggled drunkenly into the hut.

The girl holding the boy's arm drew the black cloth farther over her face and seemed somehow to become smaller. She trembled visibly as he staggered towards her.

"*Ondoka*—clear out," he shouted to the girl.

I moved round the bed to face him.

He stood looking owlishly at me, and then a strong arm came from behind and grabbed him by the shoulder and dragged him outside. There was quite a bit of shouting and then I heard someone spit out "*Punghati!*" Then came a spate of words.

I looked across at Mboga, but he was busy distilling more water and seemed to have noticed nothing unusual.

The boy had relaxed sufficiently for him to be turned on his side for the removal of the last batch of ant-heads.

As we lowered him back again I looked up at the girl who was helping. There was a tenseness about her bearing. For a moment the cloth slipped and I caught a glimpse of a drawn face and a pair of beautiful eyes. She crouched intent on supporting the small boy's arm.

The fluid was running steadily into his veins. I added more to the transfusion flask and turned to speak to the girl. Her face and bearing had been strangely familiar, but she had disappeared and Mboga was in her place.

Muttering came from the watching group as the stethoscope was placed over the child's chest. The heart was beating reasonably well now and the little fellow was out of danger.

"Who's child is he, Mboga?"

"He is the son of the brother of the Chief, Bwana."

A man with a red blanket over his shoulder came forward. "Great One, he is my child. We have praise for your help; truly your medicines are of great strength."

Again there was a commotion at the door and an entirely unusual figure forced his way to the front. A buffalo-skin head-dress, which somehow reminded me of Napoleon's three-cornered hat, covered his head and shaded a singularly glittering pair of eyes. Dangling from his neck was a blue and white enamel teapot lid, and his wrists were adorned with bottle-tops threaded on giraffe's hair. About his waist

was a cloth that was a peculiar patch-work of calico and hessian bearing the trade marks of popular brands of flour and sugar. In a deep rasping voice he said:

"The Europeans slew *nhokwa nhokwa* and the ancestors show their wrath by sending the ants."

I identified *nhokwa nhokwa* with the great turkey-like bird that we had eaten with such enthusiasm for our evening meal.

There was a charm around the child's neck, a length of greasy string with a piece of hardwood tied to it. Similar charms were about his ankles.

"Surely it is a bad thing when the medicine of witchdoctor is insufficient to control the wrath of the ancestors!" I shot back at him in the same dialect.

Using still another language Mboga said, "*Heh*, truly the charms of that animated rubbish-heap do not seem to affect ants, Bwana."

I turned to the father of the child. "Let him rest, Great One, keep him away from noise. I will leave medicine for him to swallow. Remove these ones from the hut."

The witchdoctor was the last to leave; he radiated hostility. Again I turned to the father.

"Great One, it is the custom to pay the witchdoctor for his medicine?"

He looked at me with wide eyes. "Bwana, but how shall I pay for what you have done for my son. Do you desire cattle?"

I shook my head. "No, but I want someone to guide me to the place called *Ha-ndege*, The Place of Birds."

A look of consternation came over his face.

"But, Bwana, this thing is not possible."

"And yet your son lives because of the medicines that we gave him!"

"Bwana, we must speak more of this matter," he muttered.

He looked towards the door, obviously terrified, lest anyone had heard my request.

Drums started to beat in the village; I could picture that teapot lid moving from side to side as the muscular arms of the witchdoctor beat on the zebra-hide drum.

There was a rhythm in these drums that brought out goose-pimples. The hurricane lantern seemed only to make the darkness denser. We were conscious of curious eyes peering at us out of the darkness.

"*Heee!*" grunted Mboga as we went down the path and passed the last of the huts.

"We have the swamp and the dense strip of jungle to travel through, *yoh*, I would rather do that any night than pass between the huts of this village, *ehhh*, it gives me the creeps!"

The words were hardly out of his mouth when a hand came out of the darkness and gripped his arm.

With a gasp he dropped the lantern and we were in darkness.

There came a deep chuckle and a friendly voice we knew well.

"Bwana, it is I, Tadayo; I have one with me here who would have words for you, and you alone."

"Mboga," I ordered, "stay here, fix the lantern again and I will be with you soon."

"*Koh*," came Mboga's voice, "this is no place to be alone."

Tadayo led me by the hand through deep darkness to a place where a woman crouched in a small clearing. I switched on my electric torch, but Tadayo put his hand over it.

"Bwana, turn it off, the people of the village must not know we are here."

That moment of light had shown me a grim picture. It was the girl who had helped me. The black cloth no longer hid her features, the tumour stood out between her shoulders, and there was a great livid weal across the side of her face and over her neck and shoulder.

Tadayo's voice came softly. "Bwana, the Masai who paid cattle for her thrashed her with a hippo-hide whip because of the words that she spoke the other night at the village when you showed pictures. At the moment he has drunk much beer and his wisdom has departed and she has strong desire that you should see her trouble."

In the darkness my fingers traced the edge of that tumour. It was the size of a three-months-old baby, an ugly, cumbersome thing, and yet there was nothing malignant or dangerous about it. The removal would be a simple surgical operation. I told her so.

"Bwana," she said, and her voice was amazingly musical, "the other burden has gone from my back."

"The other burden?" I questioned, and then realised what she was driving at.

"*Eh-heh*," she said, "the one that you can't see, but *ehh!* how you can feel it weighing your soul down and down. It's gone, Bwana, it has been explained to me, I have understood the words of God and have followed them."

Tadayo spoke urgently. "Bwana, we must return."

"Right. With the hand of God upon our planning, we will remove that burden from your back, Mzito; make no mistake, God looks after his own children when they let Him."

There were whispered good-byes, and two shadows disappearing into the deeper darkness. I went back to an impatient Mboga.

"What was it all about, Bwana?"

I told him. He drew a deep breath.

"Bwana, have you ever felt your heart calling for somebody?"

CHAPTER X

ELEPHANTS

IT was a strange walk back to the camp. The moonlight was pale, the hurricane lantern did little more than contribute a square yard of indefinite light. The crickets and the frogs were in fine voice, and from the rising ground beyond the swamp came the roar of lions.

Such an amazing change had occurred in Mboga that he was quite unaware of the sinister nature of the night. He overflowed enthusiasm.

"Bwana, I want four hundred shillings."

"Four hundred shillings, Vegetable! What for?"

"I want to buy someone."

"You want to buy *what*?" I swung him round and held the lantern so that his face was in close-up. He dropped his eyes and looked very uncomfortable.

"I want to buy a wife, Bwana."

"Buy a wife! You can't do that, you . . ."

"Bwana, for those shillings I can buy her freedom."

"Buy her freedom certainly, but beyond that you can't go, Mboga."

He nodded. "Truly, Bwana, to get her away from these people is the first step, for she lives in worse than misery; the ways of the man who paid money to her relations for her are the ways of a hyena. He bought her cheap because of her burden." Mboga spat so forcibly that I almost expected sparks to leap up from the path.

So worked up was he that he tripped over the shaft of his spear and fell into a bed of nettles. I choked back my laughter as he struggled back on to the path. His voice was heavy with irony.

"*Yoh*, Bwana, you bear the sorrows of others with great fortitude."

Then the corners of his mouth twisted. "*Kumbe*, Bwana,

nettles are a plant of small joy truly. *Cibite*—let's go, let's move on fast."

I held him back. "Listen to words of wisdom, O Spinach. Do not the wise ones of our tribe have a proverb, *haraka haraka haina baraka*—hurry, hurry, has no blessing."

Mboga froze into a black statue. "Look, Bwana . . ."

Less than a quarter of a mile away in the deep swamp were the moving backs of a hundred elephant.

"*Kah*," he whispered, "they move this way, Bwana; quickly, let's climb this great rock."

There was something ghostlike in the way the great beasts moved past. We crouched on the edge of the boulder, fascinated.

I heard a gulp from Mboga and my heart stood completely

still when something heavy gripped my shoulder from the darkness. I could have sworn it was an elephant's trunk, but a voice came softly out of the shadow.

"*Kah*, it is only I, Kali; it is in the goodness of God that you are safe."

I nodded. "Truly, but I think it is all right up here."

But Kali's thankfulness was due to another cause.

"Bwana," he contorted his large face, "does not my tooth ache with strength?"

Mboga's whisper came. "*Kah*, our safety surely weighs heavily upon your shoulders! First you cover us with goose-pimples, and cause sweat to start from our skin, and then you say that your tooth aches. You worry about us with strength, truly!"

Kali chuckled quietly, placing his hand on Mboga's shoulder.

"*Kah*," gulped the houseboy, drawing back, "take your huge front foot from the spot where the nettles bit me."

"Quietly," whispered Kali, "the country is full of elephant. I will lead you back in darkness by a path that does not cross the way of the creatures who have a tail at each end. Bwana Kodaki is in a special place waiting for dawn that he may take photographs. Bwana Johnson is with him, but they want you to use the small machine which collects sound from the air."

I nodded. We put out the lantern and followed Kali through deep darkness. How he found his way I don't know. There were still two hours before dawn. The first was spent returning to the camp, while the second was full of professional activity, which consisted in the soundless extraction of what Kali termed the enemy in his jaw.

Instructions had been left that whatever was done must be done in complete silence, and our lighting was nothing but a very dim lantern.

Not a hundred feet away, elephants wallowed in the mud, trumpeting conversationally.

Working largely by a sense of feel, I injected round Kali's tooth. He whispered to me, "Bwana, this is a strange medicine; death spreads through my face."

"Not death, Kali, painlessness, now open wide."

Mboga leant over and said, "If you bite the Bwana, Kali, I'll bite you."

An elephant trumpeted shrilly behind.

"Quiet," said Mboga, "have courage."

I grappled with the tooth, and a few minutes later Kali was inspecting a complete molar.

I rubbed my wrist. "I'd as soon pull a tusk from one of those noisy brutes below as do that again."

As if they regarded that as an insult, the elephants suddenly moved on, this time crashing through the undergrowth, dragging trees down as they went. Kali led me down to the place where our two friends were concealed.

Bill was a very disappointed man. The Colonel squatted on a camp-stool and said, "You had better get back higher up, Doctor. There will be another lot along in a few minutes' time; these herds don't water together. Get the tape-recorder going."

I nodded. "We've already recorded a thousand feet from that last elephant choir."

"Good; well, keep it going, keep well out of sight up there. We may be here for the rest of the day; we can't afford a movement if another herd comes and the sunlight with them."

All day long the elephant sported in the swamp; they trumpeted and flapped their ears and squirted trunkfuls of water over their backs.

White egrets that looked like bleached seagulls walked among them. It was a noisy elephant day without any special highlight until a high-pitched scream came from well behind the herd.

Bill swung his camera round in time to catch a large female trying to manœuvre a baby elephant into a suitable pool of mud. The youngster was not enthusiastic, so mother pushed him along gently with her knees.

Suddenly the little fellow, squealing shrilly, broke away and ran. The mother swung her trunk round and caught him by his tail, then, going gently into reverse, she backed into the water, taking her protesting offspring with her.

Once in the water he stood still, whimpering, while muddy water by the trunkful cascaded over his back and ears.

Suddenly the little elephant seemed to realize the ordeal was over. He splashed hurriedly out of the swamp, squealing.

Three large elephant turned and looked after him with that expression which says, 'What are children coming to these days!'

Bill was gleefully filming it all, and I could imagine his headline, 'Elephant's bath-day'.

At sundown, two weary, unshaven figures walked up from what Bill called 'the lurk'.

"Two thousand feet of elephant, Doc," grinned the photographer. "Did you see Ma elephant washing behind junior's ears?"

Before I could answer, Mboga appeared with two five-gallon drums full of hot water, and in carefully rehearsed English said:

"Water bath, sirs?"

A few minutes later, a most savoury smell started to proceed from his cooking area. I was most intrigued and went to investigate.

"What have you been up to, Vegetable?"

"Bwana, *ngubi* the warthog walked with small care and the spear of . . ."

He stopped suddenly and changed his whole wording. "A hunter round here killed a warthog with a spear only this morning. I am cooking it in a way that should bring joy to the stomach of Bwana Kodaki."

I looked at the thick steaks that were grilling; they certainly looked the last word in palatable pork.

"Listen, Spinach, if you would have the stomach of Bwana Kodaki to sing, it is of great importance that the steak should be tender. How are you to know that this warthog is not one of the elders of his tribe and that this fact is not reflected in his carcase?"

Mboga smiled. "Bwana, this hunter who is my friend," he looked at me with a question in his eye, but I took no notice, "he and I cut with skill. The meat was wrapped in paw-paw leaves and the seeds of the paw-paw also were put round it. It has rested in a cool place under a great rock. And look, Bwana, I have made a special relish for the meat. I learned the words from old Tembo, the cook."

He uncovered a basin, and there was undoubted apple-sauce.

"And look, Bwana."

He demonstrated a noble collection of French-fried potato chips.

"*Hongo*, you have gone to very special trouble, Mboga."

"*Eh-heh*, Bwana," he smiled, "there is joy in bringing satisfaction to the Great One, and also I have strong need of four hundred shillings. How better can one bargain than after a good meal? A stomach at peace means a relaxed pocket."

He carefully turned the steaks. "Bwana, I have set the table, and in a very few minutes all will be ready."

I strolled across to where two tired men had taken jungle

showerbaths and were no little refreshed. The Colonel raised his eyebrows, and his nostrils twitched. Bill Bailey, however, was much more vocal.

"Say, that's poetry to the nose. I suppose that Mboga is producing bacon and eggs, the great British breakfast, for my supper? Well, it could be worse, but oh, I think"—he closed his eyes—"of a little place in Arizona and luscious ham steak three-quarters of an inch thick!" Dreamily he looked out into the sunset.

Mboga, dressed in a long, flowing white kanzu, and again using his inaccurate English, said, "Dinner is swerved, sir."

"Say, where's Ibrahim?" asked Bill.

"By special request, this is an all Mboga show."

The Colonel nodded, but Bill's grin was expansive. It grew even more so when he saw what was on his plate.

The Colonel's eye gleamed. "Apple-sauce, eh?"

Some time later, as he put down his knife and fork, he smiled across at me.

"A notable meal, Doctor."

Bill, however, was looking doubtfully at the coffee-pot. "You've said it, Colonel, but it could be ruined if that pot contains what I'm afraid it does. All day long I've been looking at mud stirred up by elephants, and . . ." He paused.

Mboga with his head on one side was watching with no little concern. Bill picked up his cup and tasted. He looked up at Mboga and said, "Say, you deserve the order of the golden skillet."

The African sensed the meaning, but asked quietly, "Bwana, what exactly are his words?"

"He issues praise of a high order, Mboga."

A slow smile spread. "Bwana, do you think the bait for my trap was good?"

"Wonderful! I'm all for more traps of this sort."

"Then, Bwana, when shall I come to sell my leopard-skin?"

"Now! It may be that Bwana Kodaki has eaten with too much enthusiasm; before long his stomach will bite him. Now is the time."

Mboga disappeared discreetly and returned with a beautiful leopard-skin. My mind went back to another trap that had nearly landed us in disaster.

"Great One," said Mboga, "I have strong need of many shillings."

I translated.

Bill sat back in his chair and listened.

"This is a leopard-skin without flaw," said Mboga. "A skin such as this is only for a chief or someone of great importance. Truly it is food for the eyes."

He displayed it over his arm to good advantage.

"What's it worth, Colonel?"

"It's a beautiful skin; I should say at least two hundred shillings."

Mboga's eyes flickered.

"About thirty-five dollars," murmured Bill. He leaned forward in his chair, but before he could say a word we all were startled by the uncannily close laughter of a hyena.

Mboga rushed back to his fire in time to find that the portions of warthog which he had selected for himself, Ibrahim and Kali, had departed in the unhygienic mouth of an elderly hyena.

Bill was vastly amused, but didn't for a moment show it.

"Vegetable," he said, "you deserve better things than that. I will give you two hundred shillings for the skin of the leopard, and a further two hundred if you can trap a hyena for me in such a way that it will make a cute movie."

I translated this. "The Bwana has strong desire that you should make a hyena-trap of skill, one which will produce food for the camera."

Mboga nodded his head vigorously. "*Nghu'lumba muno muno*—I praise him greatly."

"Bill, he says that he sure will."

For two hours we sat round the table listening to Colonel Johnson talk of elephants.

As he got up from the table he said, "We must get plenty of sleep; we must be up and in that 'lurk' of yours at 3.0 a.m., Bailey; we cannot afford to be a moment later."

CHAPTER XI

STONE

THE jeep skidded violently; soft mud went flying.

"Keep her moving," urged Colonel Johnson.

We jumped out and pushed. Slowly the sturdy little machine moved forward, then unexpectedly the bonnet tilted. We sank up to our knees and the jeep was mudborne.

Over the hill came Mboga and twenty Africans.

"Spinach has the useful habit of appearing in the nick of time," chuckled Bill, putting away his camera.

To him, being bogged was a chance for human interest photography.

"Good title for this spool: 'Too thick to swim, too thin to walk'."

Kali had fixed a stout rope to the front axle.

"Bwana"—Mboga came squelching towards me—"M'falme, the chief of the village, has a sickness of great pain. For him the witchdoctor's medicines and charms have small power; he has strong fear of death."

"Get them to pull us out of this bog and we'll come at once."

Mboga passed on the instructions, and those with him waded into the mud. Some lifted, some pulled, others pushed, but all sang. Mud flew everywhere; the smell was overpowering.

"*Sukuma!*—Push!" yelled Kali.

"*Na vilungu!*—With strength!" urged Mboga.

With a horrid sucking sound we slithered out and plunged forward uphill.

A lean athletic man, with mud dripping from his legs, called to us. "Follow us, Bwana, this is the road that leads to the village."

With the escort trotting beside us, or hacking a track through the thornbush, we were soon moving at a fair pace over very rough country. For a quarter of a mile the whole

F

77

undergrowth had been trampled down by elephant; then there was a hold-up while a fallen tree was manhandled out of the way.

At last the grass-roofed beehive huts came into view.

"*Hee*, Bwana," called Mboga, grabbing up the medical case.

Outside the most imposing hut was a group of village elders. I greeted them ceremonially. They replied suitably.

From inside the hut came the most dramatic groans. To force my way in would have been fatal. Bill, who was behind me, was all ready for immediate action.

"Get going," came his voice.

One tall old man led us into the gloom.

"No photographs in here," I whispered, "we're on rather delicate ground."

Bill nodded.

On a bed made from rough-cut timber and raw hide tossed a wild-eyed man.

Mboga whispered in my ear. "It's renal colic, Bwana."

He grinned at me. "Shall I rub his back with the medicine that smells?"

I nodded. He proceeded to do so with vigour, and grunted in the most professional way as he massaged.

"Quite a doctor, isn't he?" murmured Bill.

"Someone has been coaching him; he doesn't know enough for those comments by himself."

Behind me came a muttering from some twenty Africans crammed into the back of the hut.

In Swahili I asked a number of questions. "Did he have the pain in the back? Did the pain move to this place, to that place? Had he been passing blood?" It took a time for the answer because the chief tossed from side to side in agony, groaning and making the African sound of pain—"*Eeeeeeh . . .!*"

I asked Mboga. "They think its witchcraft?"

"*Eh-heh*, Bwana. They say it is *pepo*, an evil spirit. As you go out, look and you will see the little spirit-house that they have built outside so that the ancestors may be kept quiet."

"It's a little rough to blame the ancestors for this. He's got a little stone that's trying to get out from his kidney, and *yoh! heeh*, the pain! But if we can make the small pipe that runs down from his kidney become relaxed and loose, the stone will drop down."

"*Yoh*," said Mboga, "have you the medicine?"

"Yes, here it is."

I rubbed M'falme's arm with a small swab and sharply pushed in a needle, and he yelled. "*Yoh! Kah! Heh*, it hurts, I'm stabbed!"

From farther back in the hut came the glint of a spear. I stood up.

"Great One, the medicine enters your body through *sindano*—the needle. It takes five minutes for it to have its main work. Lie quietly."

There was a sense of hostility in that hut which you could almost touch. I could see that spear, stationary, pointing in my direction. Seldom has time gone slower. The chief lay there moaning.

Then a drum started to beat with a slow uneasy rhythm. A murmuring came from the darkness just outside the circle of light thrown by the smoky hurricane lamp.

"*Eeh, eeh, eeh*, the pain," groaned M'falme.

He sat up. One hand was clasped over the small of his back, the other caressed his thin abdomen. The sweat stood out on his forehead, his eyes were pain-ridden. About his neck was a charm. There was a piece of greasy string tied round his chest. This was a charm with a different importance. About his ankles were further charms made from goats' skin. I thought of the futility of it, and then a voice said:

"His pain does not change. The medicine of the Bwana has no strength, it's . . . ."

Then the chief interrupted. "*Ooooooh*," he sighed, "that's better, pain ceases to tear my vitals. Truly this is medicine, Bwana."

I could see the spear silently lowered and struck into the ground. The drums kept on beating outside. For ten minutes I listened to their rhythm and then turned to our patient.

"Great One, what of your pain now?"

"Bwana, it is reduced in my back, it aches, but the pain as though the spirits would drag me apart has gone."

"Great One, drink much water."

A gourd was brought and he drank at least a quart of it. From the medical bag I took two pills.

"Now swallow these."

He did so without question.

"Before long, you will suddenly get a great pain and as that pain comes, you will pass a stone. This thing is the cause of your trouble."

"*Yoh*, Bwana, how do you know these things?"

Mboga replied. "The Bwana is one of wisdom and of much training. He knows the causes of trouble. He knows the medicines that stop the pain, he . . ."

The chief let out a hollow moan, then shrieked and foamed at the mouth. There was a time of intense activity.

When it was all over successfully, Mboga held a roughened object shaped like a date-stone in his fingers.

"*Kah*, so that was the cause."

M'falme lay back, shocked and gasping.

"Rub it on your cheek, Vegetable."

He did so. "*Yoh*, it scratches."

"Imagine passing that down the fine passages from your kidney, passages that are more tender than the lining of your nose."

Mboga rolled his eyes. The chief groaned, and whispered, "Bwana, truly your medicine has great strength."

"*Naheeh!*" came a chorus of voices from the back of the room, "the Bwana is truly a *fundi*—an expert."

CHAPTER XII

COBRA AND WORSE

As we went out into the sunlight, a strange figure came out of the doorway opposite us. He walked stiffly, the corner of his mouth jerked spasmodically, his eye twitched, and there was an unsteady tremble about his hand.

As we watched him, Bill suddenly swatted his bare arm violently, and at the same instant I felt a burning pain in the back of my neck.

"*Eh-heh*," said Mboga, "truly this is a country of tsetse fly."

The sick man stood in front of us, his hand and forearm uncontrollable. In a thick voice, he said:

"Bwana, have you medicine for my trouble?"

A palm-leaf mat was brought and I lay him on it, most carefully examining the whole of his nervous system. There were glands under his arm, glands at the back of his neck, his spleen was large, there were glands in his groin. As the examination went on, I could see that it was too late. Sleeping-sickness had done its damage.

The old man looked up with hopeless eyes.

The photographer raised his eyebrows.

I shook my head. "Can't do a thing, Bill, not a thing."

"*Hongo*, Bwana," said one of the villagers, "there are many, many in our houses who have sickness of this sort."

"Tomorrow," I said, "when we come back to visit the chief again, cause them to be brought that we may see them."

"*Eh-heh*, Bwana."

Next morning the chief was sitting in the shade in an ancient deck-chair. Beneath the mango tree opposite him were a group of people. He motioned to them to come across one by one.

The first was an old man, one leg drawn up, stiff, paralysed. They carried him across on a crude stretcher. He was almost unconscious, and his eyes were glazed.

The chief pointed with his chin. "He's been like this for many days, Bwana."

"*Hongo*, are there others like him in the village Great One?"

"*Eh-heh*, there are three others, and perhaps twenty have died since the harvest was planted."

Behind me came Bill's voice. "Is all this sleeping-sickness, Doc?"

"Yes, that fellow we saw yesterday is incurable, and these folk are right at the very end of the road. You can see the havoc that the tsetse fly produces."

I turned to the chief. "Great One, this is a disease caused by the bite of *m'bungo*, the tsetse fly."

Mboga caught my eye and raised his eyebrows. I nodded. He grinned, and disappeared outside.

"*M'bungo* is an insect of great danger." I turned to the chief and those who were crowded round him. "By his bite he plants within your body a *dudu* which grows and breeds. As it multiplies, trouble starts. First the place of the bite becomes sore and itchy and there is fever. The desire for food is gone."

"*Eh-heh*," said the chief, "these things we know, Bwana, but this is not the result of the bite of a *dudu*."

"Oh, yes it is. It is the reason that these people are ill and that many have died."

The chief shook his head. "Bwana, this cannot be."

"Truly, Great One, I know there are those of the tribe who say that it is the work of spirits, but with my machine that makes little things appear big, I can show you the cause."

At that moment, the chief's small son ran in and stood beside him. The child looked sick. He huddled close to his father and I could see he was shivering.

"Great One," I said, "look at your child. Run your hand behind his neck and see if there is not swelling."

He did so and nodded.

"He has the disease, probably. At this stage, we can help him, we can save his life. Delay, and he will become like the man outside. Delay longer, and he will be like the two old men that we just looked at."

Mboga came through the door holding two pieces of wood. He whispered to me and put one into my hand.

"Great One," I said, "you see this wood."

The people crowded round.

"Behold, it looks to have strength, but hold it in your hand and it is too light to be as wood should be."

The chief nodded and muttered the word "*mimehe*".

"Truly," I said, and broke it across my knee; there was a cascade of rotten wood and white ants.

"Many days have those white ants been in that wood," said the chief.

"Truly," I replied, "but look at this piece."

Mboga handed me the second piece of wood. It felt heavy. I did my best to break it across my knee but it was solid and firm and yet along the side of it you could see the place where white ants had started on their job.

"*Yoh*," said the chief, "*mimehe* the white ant has done little trouble there."

"How would you suggest that I stop him doing more?"

"*Koh*," they said, "you could put medicine down the hole that he travels."

"True, and what then?"

"That would kill him."

"What I'm suggesting, chief, is that your child is like this piece of wood. The old man is like that piece of wood." I pointed to the debris on the ground. "We can save the child. The old man has gone too far."

A long-drawn-out scream came from the other end of the village. The men had grasped their knobbed sticks and their spears and rushed to the spot.

We followed, Bill was hugely excited. He had his tripod set and was shooting films in a moment.

It certainly was a drama. A hooded cobra, its tongue flashing in and out, reared up and spat at those who circled round it. They chanted and swayed and spat back at it.

It turned this way and that, then suddenly its long, flexible body surged forward and the hooded head struck.

The wary African lad immediately in its path leaped backward and the attacking circle moved backward and reformed.

The snake was obviously dazed. Again and again it struck viciously till one of the villagers leapt forward and brought his stick down, whack! on the back of the reptile.

Fiercely it turned on its assailant, its movement slowed by the blow. Even as it turned, another stick struck it higher up, and another, and another.

As a long pole was pushed under its body to carry it to the rubbish heap the chief said, "Behold, see its fangs! Behind those are little sacs of poison, in which is enough poison to kill ten of us."

"*Kumbe*, Great One," asked the boy, "are there many who die through the bite of *nzoka* the snake?"

I stood forward and, speaking as loudly as was wise, I said, "Oh, Chief, your words are full of wisdom; listen therefore to the story of M'bungo the tsetse fly and Nzoka the snake.

"In another village the skilful ones had killed a snake. The people rejoiced, and in the late afternoon, Ihowe the crow and his relations feasted upon the dead body of Nzoka.

"Deep in the thornbush, over a pool of water, was M'bungo the chief of the tsetse fly and many of his nimble tribe. One flew in swiftly on his flashing wings, and said, 'News from the village. They have killed Nzoka the snake with sticks and much shouting and have thrown his body with disdain upon the rubbish heap where Ihowe the crow eats his fill. Alive they fear him, but dead they fear him not.'

"A young fly flew into the air full of tsetse anger. 'Snakes they fear, but us, ah no. They grumble at our biting, they swish at us with small branches. They scratch the place where our teeth have gone through their skin and curse with many words, but they do not *fear* us.'

"M'bungo folded his wings.

"'Peace,' he said, 'save your words. Snakes may kill a hundred people in the whole of this country in a year. We kill a hundred times that number.

"'Snakes may drive them from a house in fear but we make great stretches of country so deadly that no man may safely enter it.'

"The elderly insect became highly excited. 'It is our heritage, O tsetse flies, by our biting to pass on this large poison.'

"There was the excited buzzing a swarm of flies and then again words.

"'Our teeth are smaller than any snake's but a hundred times more deadly, the larger poison behind our small teeth is more to be feared than many a gallon of snake venom.'

"Three times he flew round the branch where his companions rested in ecstasy, and coming to roost again, said, 'They don't realize it.

"'They don't realize it, they don't realize it.

"'Therein lies our strength.'"

As I finished my story there was a nodding of heads and a hum of conversation.

"*Hongo*," said the chief. "Bwana, this is food for the ears; also the words will stick in our minds."

"Great One, I have joy to visit you and to give my medicines; before we return, however, there is a medicine of strength that will give comfort to those with bad ulcers."

"*Heeh!*" cried a man with an ugly and varied collection of sores and ulcers. "Bwana, let me taste this medicine; my skin has no joy, not even a little."

The chief nodded. "These are good words."

"Truly, Great One, this man shall have the medicine; the others of your village may see how it works and when I return others may want it also."

There was a lot of conversation and we were surrounded with curious faces as a large dose of penicillin was given.

The man grinned up at me as the needle was withdrawn.

"Bwana, many shall hear of this medicine, and many more will clamour for it when you return."

We were given an enthusiastic send-off after the chief had presented me with two skinny chickens and a gourd full of eggs, ten of which later proved to be bad.

CHAPTER XIII

LEOPARD

BILL sat at the safari table, insects swarmed round the pressure-lamp, the crickets were hard at it. From far over the plain came that dramatic noise, the roar of a lion, and from very close at hand, the strident howl of a hyena. The photographer shook his fist in the direction of the sound.

Some distance away, Mboga and Ibrahim were doing the washing-up, while Tembo the cook was hanging the meat from a limb of one of the trees where it would be out of reach of both leopard and hyena.

The hyena gave tongue again, this time considerably closer. Bill stood up and shook both his fists at the appropriate patch of darkness.

"Howl, you stinker, you'll catch it soon. Not only will I make you laugh out of the other side of your face, but a million people will laugh at you too, you scavenger. A pretty picture you'll look in a trap on the movies."

I could hear chuckles coming from the kitchen end of things. Colonel Johnson and Kali were cleaning guns. I sat looking into the fire, enjoying to the full the nightly symphony which the jungle provided free.

The Colonel packed up his kit and came across.

"Well, the supply lorry arrives tomorrow. Suliman the Indian is a very good fellow—always likes to take a little meat with him. Just as well we shot those buck and those zebra."

I had been watching the firelight playing on the faces of the two washers-up, and was amazed to see a most strange tenseness come over Ibrahim for a moment, and then it was gone.

Bill was holding a sheet of paper in his hand.

"Come over beside the fire, Colonel. I want to read you the script of how to influence hyenas.

"First, there is a close-up of Mboga demonstrating his trap.

"Then a long shot of the jeep setting out at dawn, and the animals on the horizon. Then we could use some of those mediums and close-ups of you stalking with Kali, and a close-up as you pick your animal and shoot.

"Then a rear view of Kali carrying the animal. After that we will concentrate on the hyena-trap."

As he spoke the words, into the lamplight slunk a rakish-looking brute whose hindquarters looked crippled, and an ugly reek of long dead flesh came from it.

I saw the muscles of Kali's arm ripple, with barely an action he threw a hunting-knife, the blade whistling through

the air, but the hyena moved to one side, as though the whole act was planned. It lifted its head and produced that eerie sound called hyena laughter.

Mboga, from under the tree where he was washing, threw an enamel plate. The spotted scavenger watched it hurtle past, with a look on its ugly face that was contemptuous. It scratched, and strolled away impudently into the jungle.

"Oh, brother," breathed Bill, "what fun to have you in a bag, what a stimulus you are to a script-writer." He ran his fingers through his hair and set to work again with his pencil.

"Hateful brutes," said the Colonel, "they kill the newly-born and the mother before she is strong enough to defend herself." He shrugged his shoulders. "We need an early night to-night; before turning in I'll make sure that zebra-skin is properly pegged out."

No hyena made itself obvious that night.

Once, well before dawn, there were scratching noises and the smell of moist earth. Sleepily I put this down to our friend, the ant-bear.

I woke to hear angry voices. The zebra skin had disappeared.

Quite a deep hole had been scraped underneath my camp

stretcher. Bill and the Colonel were walking round, looking intently at the ground.

"Come and look in here," I called. "The brute has dug a hole underneath my camp-bed."

Mboga came running to my tent. He stood outside for a long moment, then speaking in rapid Swahili said,

"Bwana, my leopard-skin money has been stolen. I buried it under here." He pointed to where the camp-bed had stood. "I thought it the safest of hiding-places."

The Colonel bent down on one knee. "Look here—a different variety of hyena—see these?"

He pointed to human footprints. It was obvious that the first toe was missing.

"It's that fellow Simba up to his thieving tricks again. His name may mean lion, but he has something of a hyena in him.

Mboga stooped and looked at the ground and shrugged his shoulders.

At breakfast the Colonel said: "Mboga's taking this very calmly."

"He is indeed. For a moment I thought he was going to say something in defence of his friend Simba. You know, Colonel, that fellow is the wrong shape somehow to fit into this thieving."

The hunter shrugged his shoulders. "Those footprints are hard to explain away; they're *facts*—evidence."

Bill got up from the table irritably. "Say, I am allergic to hyenas of all variety. What about some action? Let's shoot that model trap sequence. We'll work over there beside that thorn tree; the light's just right."

In a few Swahili words I passed this on to Mboga. He soon had a string bag opened and flattened out. At six points on its circumference lengths of thick twine were attached. These were all joined together, and attached was a long rope that was carried over the limb of a tree and quite a sizeable stone was hung on the far end. A stout string held the stone from falling. Slash this and the stone fell, pulling up the string bag, and the trap was sprung.

The camera whirred as Mboga put things into place. Bill looked up.

"Say, it would be good if we had some critter that would walk into this miniature trap."

Mboga grinned, understanding enough to get the sense of what was said. He put his hand inside his shirt and pulled out a chameleon. The odd creature swayed along the ground, changing colour as it walked over the grass.

"Swell," came Bill's voice from behind the camera.

Suddenly the chameleon was in the centre of the trap. Mboga's hand holding a sharp knife swept down, the cord was cut, the stone dropped and the trap shot off the ground with the chameleon struggling grotesquely.

"Swell again," grinned Bill, "now for the real thing."

The leg of zebra and the tin containing the offal was let down from the tree. It stank vilely and flies rose in clouds.

"It's going to be late afternoon," said the Colonel, "when the hyenas will come. We had better choose a spot where the light will be good at that hour."

He and Bill carefully planned out the setting.

Fifty-foot thorn trees were high overhead; underneath them were tussocks of quite tall grass. On the gradual slope up towards the camp were some tall, very green trees with smaller saplings beneath them.

Kali set to work to build a camouflage shelter behind which we would wait for action.

Mboga's preparations were most elaborate and careful. He inspected his large trap, a circular piece of netting, eight feet in diameter—and the ropes were placed with great care.

"*Yoh*," he smiled, "traps! How I like traps!"

He tied the main rope to a stone which was so heavy that he and Kali had the greatest difficulty in hauling it up the the tree. With the utmost care, the trigger rope was tied, and dry grass was spread over both trap and ropes. Mboga wanted to sprinkle the whole thing with some of the highly-smelling contents of the kerosene tin.

"Not yet, Vegetable; wait till the last minute. My nose has small joy to be in that place of concealment.

Mboga laughed.

"Listen," I said, "you have behaved very well today, Vegetable, in the matter of the stolen money."

He smiled. "Bwana, my mind is taken up with traps."

He seemed to have a second meaning tucked away somewhere in his voice. I looked carefully at him, but there was no sign of anything in his expression. He was the same old Mboga, cheerful, but not very subtle-looking.

"*Hongo*," he said, "listen, Bwana, a lorry is coming."

A few minutes later over the crest of the hill came a vehicle. The Colonel stepped forward to greet the smiling Indian who sprang from behind the wheel.

"Good day, Suliman; what have you brought for us?"

"There is a bag of mail, sir, also some fruit and some vegetables and some tins of food as instructed."

"Thank you; I have shot a little meat for you."

"Thank you so very much. There are some necessary repairs I must make to my vehicle, and then with your permission, I will leave at sunset."

"We are having a little hyena hunting this afternoon, Suliman—I don't know whether you are interested in hyenas?"

The Indian smiled. "It would give me great pleasure to watch. I find that the hyena is a creature of small enchantment."

Bill grinned. "He's sure right."

"*Saa kenda*—the ninth hour," came Mboga's voice, "it is time now to go to the trap. Would you first drink tea, Bwana?"

I nodded.

Bill had spent the heat of the day in getting his cameras exactly as he wanted them. All three were loaded and all placed so that he could film every angle of the drama.

Kali dipped his hand into the fly-surrounded kerosene tin and poured some of the juices over his feet.

Bill held his nose.

"Say, no hyena would smell Kali above that."

The African threw the offal around like ground bait, and then tipped the whole stinking mess over the leg of zebra which was in the very centre of the trap.

"Come on," said Bill, "into the lurk."

There was silent activity as final preparations were made. My particular task was to record the sound. I made sure that my microphone was where it ought to be, and that the recorder was in instant readiness.

Then came what seemed an appallingly long wait. The flies were grimly tenacious, and I have seldom seen more earwigs. Mboga carefully placed a forked stick over an outsize in centipedes.

As I crouched down behind that four-feet-high screen, my

mind went to Simba. On the face of it, he was a thief, but I could not imagine Simba stealing money from Mboga. Whichever way I looked at it, it still did not fit into the picture.

Then I thought of the sly twinkle in Mboga's eye and his talk about traps. There was something I hadn't grasped about it.

Between the tree tops I could see vultures circling. The shadows were beginning to lengthen. Joe carefully took readings with his light-meter.

Suddenly Kali became tense. He pointed with his chin to the north. A huge grin came over Mboga's face.

Above us was a tree with peculiar beanpods on it that made a whirring sound as the wind blew. It made excellent sound-camouflage for the camera.

With the telephoto lens, Bill was shooting every step of the hyena's approach. It stopped for a moment warily, looked up at the vultures, and then, at a slinking trot, came right up to the meat. We could see saliva running from its ugly mouth. The second camera started whirring in harmony with the tree above us.

The Colonel raised his finger, Mboga's knife flashed. The tape recorder was going and it collected two almost simultaneous sounds. The thump of the stone hitting the ground and the startled scream of the hyena as it was jerked high into the air, helpless in the net. It struggled, snarling and yelping, its legs came through holes in the net and scratched futilely at the air.

The long silence was broken, there was laughter and noise and strong reaction. Bill was moving the tripod of his camera and murmuring, "Oh brother, oh brother!"

Kali started to beat a drum, and Mboga to play his *ilimba*. Colonel Johnson spoke quietly behind me.

"Look over there, Doctor, at that big heavily-leafed tree —do you see?"

Bill caught the words, swung his camera round expectantly. The sun came through a gap and spotlighted the deep green. As the leaves stirred we could see a vague figure keeping close to the dark trunk.

"What's that guy up to," whispered Bill, "and who is he, anyway?"

From high up in the trees came the warning bark of a monkey.

"Put the glasses on that guy, Colonel, he's . . ."

The hunter drew in his breath sharply. "He's stopped for a moment, he's groping in a hollow in the tree. There, he's got it."

With difficulty, the hand dragged out a once-white canvas bag, and then the thief disappeared from view.

Again came the warning monkey-bark. The hyena was whimpering in its cringing way.

"Simba collecting his loot, eh! Planning to stow away in Suliman's lorry and relying on this hyena-show to act as a diversion!"

There was a chill note in the Englishman's voice.

The climber, naked except for a black loincloth, was barely visible in the deep-green foliage. Suddenly his profile was clearly outlined against the sky.

Bill's camera whirred and he spoke sharply. "It's not Simba at all, it's my Ibrahim! The scoundrel!—and I trusted him completely." Bill was obviously thoroughly shaken.

"So *that's* where the money went," growled the Colonel, "I'd better arrange a suitable reception-committee. And to think we have been unjustly suspecting Simba all along!"

He carefully followed every move through the glasses.

"Keep the noise going, Kali, we don't want him to know he's been seen."

Above the noise of the hyena-trap came the cackle of quail.

"There is no doubt about it's being Ibrahim; he's climbing down now."

Suddenly Kali sprang to his feet.

"Bwana, there's something else up that tree."

He thrust a rifle into Colonel Johnson's hands. The whole place was filled with the most hair-raising noises.

"Leopard," shouted the hunter, pushing the glasses towards me. They seemed to bring me within hand-touch of Ibrahim. His eyes were wide with horror; his hands clutched at the tree trunk.

The leopard's yellow skin and dark spots showed starkly against the leaves. With cold hypnotic eyes it moved purposefully along the limb, angry, snarling through bared teeth.

G

"No chance of a shot from here," came the Colonel's tense voice. "I'm moving forward. Keep behind me—leopards are the most deadly customers."

The camera whirred on without a pause.

CHAPTER XIV

ACTION

From the direction of the camp a broad-shouldered figure, with poised spear, came leaping towards the thicket, yelling to distract the leopard.

"It's Simba!" breathed Mboga.

We moved twenty yards nearer. The leopard was still a poor target, but the Colonel took careful aim.

Ibrahim grasped the bag of money and made a futile attempt to strike at the crouching animal.

The rifle shot cracked as the leopard sprang. Man and beast fell crashing through the dense foliage of the jungle tree.

A dull thud was followed by the vicious snarling of the leopard, and a hoarse scream. Then came a ringing shout, and then the evening noises were undisturbed.

We rushed forward, stumbling over rocks and through tough wiry grass.

There was ominous silence in the thicket. Again came the sound of Bill's camera as he panned it to take in one sweep a grim tableau spotlighted by a shaft of late afternoon sunlight.

Simba stood over the quivering body of Ibrahim, a blood-stained spear in his hand. Only a few feet away lay the leopard, a bullet-wound in its throat and a gaping spear gash in the left side of its flank.

"Well done, Simba," said Colonel Johnson as he bent over the great beast. "My shot was too low. In time it would have killed the creature, but while this was happening, certainly Ibrahim and perhaps one of us would have lost our lives. A leopard running amok is a terrible risk."

I was crouched beside Ibrahim. His pulse was barely beating.

"How is he, Doctor?"

95

"Barely alive. He must have fallen with the brute on top of him; he has some broken ribs and his lung's damaged, and he has lacerations from teeth and claws.

"Mboga, quickly, I want one of the doors from the hut; pull it right off the hinges. Wrench it off, kick it off. We want it for a stretcher."

Morphia was given to control pain and shock. A handkerchief served as an impromptu tourniquet.

Ibrahim groaned and tried to speak as I stopped the hæmorrhages. Kali and Mboga were beside me with the door. Simba followed with a blanket.

Gently we lifted our battered patient and carried him the hundred yards to the hut. I issued orders.

"Simba, the primus stove—we want boiling water.

"The instruments, Mboga, from the back of the three-ton truck.

"The pressure-lamp, Colonel. We want every bit of light we can get."

I scrubbed my hands in a cut-down kerosene tin. Ibrahim's arm, shoulder and chest were deeply torn by the leopard's claws. Added to this he had six ribs broken, and a fractured spine from the fall.

Hot stones from the fire, wrapped in sacking, were used as make-shift hot water bottles.

Minutes later I was operating in a forlorn effort to save a life. Shock was the primary danger. If we could overcome this, the risk of infection was still very high.

The first stage of stopping bleeding, wound-dressing, splinting and bandaging was over.

Simba asked, "What now, Bwana?"

"A transfusion now might save him."

Mboga stepped forward. "Bwana, try my blood."

The Colonel raised his eyebrows. "But he stole your money!"

Mboga stood uncomfortably for a moment and then said, "Bwana Johnson, Jesus Christ did far more than that for me. He gave His life, not just a pint of blood. I have done worse things to God than Ibrahim ever did to me."

I interrupted. "The microscope, Mboga, and the glass slides."

They were brought at the double.

Minutes flew while the blood was checked. The sterilized

emergency transfusion outfit was being unwrapped, when Simba's voice came softly.

"Bwana, look at him."

My stethoscope could pick up only very faint heart sounds. As I listened they became irregular, faltered, and then stopped.

Simba's eyes asked the question.

I nodded. "It's too late, he's gone."

The Colonel stood up and walked quietly out into the night.

Bill Bailey sat, his chin in his hands. His voice came. "That's awful; a life lost for a bag of money."

"It's happened before, Bill. Remember Judas Iscariot? He sold the Son of God for some ten dollars."

I covered the dead African's face.

Bill spoke again. "But death seems a terrible cost for a sin like that."

"That's the way it is with sin. It always pays its servants, and its wages are death, sometimes coming dramatically, like this poor chap, more often insidiously."

There was silence as I slowly washed my hands and started to boil up the instruments.

The photographer paced up and down the room. "Doc, if the leopard had taken you, if it was your body on that table, what then? Where would you be now?"

I pumped up the primus before replying.

"My body would have done its job, but the eternal part of me, my soul, would have passed through the gate called death, and I would come face to face with Almighty God, and His Son, Jesus Christ Himself, would stand forward on my behalf."

"But how do you *know*?"

From my pocket came a small Testament. I turned over the pages.

"Listen," I read, "And if we sin, we have an advocate with the Father, Jesus Christ, the righteous One; He is the propitiation—the One who paid the price—for our sins, and not for ours only, but for the sins of the whole world."

Bill nodded slowly. "Maybe," his voice was husky, "maybe He would do that for me too if I asked Him?"

"He would indeed."

I watched him walk into the darkness, his head bowed.

Mechanically I put the instruments away. Simba came over to me.

"Bwana, Kali and I will prepare a grave. Suliman and his helper Abdulla want permission to bury him, for he is a follower of the prophet."

I nodded.

Simba hesitated. "Bwana, it would be wise to deal swiftly with the matter of Mzito. The Masai might change his mind."

"Tonight, Simba?"

The African nodded vigorously.

We stood in the light of the hurricane lantern as Ibrahim was buried. As we came back to the tent, Simba stood at attention.

"Bwana Colonel, I have a word."

The Englishman smiled. "Yes, Simba."

"With your permission, Kali, Mboga and I will go to the village."

He pointed into the darkness with his chin. "We will take with us the money and buy back the girl with the tumour between her shoulders. News of today's happenings may cause great trouble and the changing of minds."

"Did you understand what he said, Bailey?"

Bill shook his head. "I wasn't listening. To think that I filmed that whole incident cold-bloodedly gives me the creeps now, and I'll have to look at it and live it over and over again."

The Colonel spoke quietly. "We were speaking of a different matter. It's life, not death. Simba wants to redeem the girl with the tumour; they want to finalize the matter tonight."

Simba nodded.

I broke in. "Suliman is staying the night. If we operate tonight she can go with him tomorrow. Simba's wife, Perisi, is a nurse. She'll look after her and do any necessary dressings."

"Sure, sure," said Bill, getting to his feet. "I'll get the rest of the money; let's get rolling."

CHAPTER XV

OPERATION

IN the firelight Bill carefully counted out the shillings.

"There are the two hundred shillings for your leopard-skin, Mboga, and these two hundred are for your most efficient hyena-trap."

A smile passed between them. Suliman came forward; in his hand were two lengths of the brightly-coloured cotton material that African women wear.

"Simba," he said, "give these to her; they will give her courage."

Kali got behind the wheel of the jeep, and the others sat behind him.

"Good hunting," cried the Colonel, as they moved on into the darkness.

Bill rigged up a series of lights and took a movie of old Tembo skinning the leopard, then we sat round the fire.

The Colonel broke the silence. "I am afraid I misjudged Simba badly. By the way, did you notice the way that poor chap had done up his toes?"

I certainly had noticed how sticking plaster had been used to lift one of Ibrahim's toes so that his footprints would be mistaken for Simba's.

"That must have been the reason why he always insisted on wearing shoes."

Colonel Johnson nodded. "It takes a lot of courage to deal with a leopard with a spear. I owe that man an apology."

"He's been doing a solid job over in that village, Colonel. Quite frankly, I was prepared to back my hunch that he was innocent, even against the evidence. Apparently, as soon as he felt he was under your suspicion, he kept right out of sight, in the way Africans can do so well. I didn't say anything, but it was fairly obvious that Simba was in the village when I dealt with the boy who was covered with ants.

Somebody prepared things in a very workmanlike way. Also the whole negotiation for the freeing of this girl has been carried through by him."

I stood up. "Excuse me, I must go and get ready for this operation."

I sterilized the instruments and rigged up a mosquito-net to keep out the insects. The lights of the jeep moved toward us through the night and faintly came the tooting of the horn.

As they came up the hill toward the camp, we could hear the sound of Mboga's *ilimba* and faint singing.

"That's an odd instrument," remarked the Colonel.

"And that's an odd tune to hear right out here in the jungle."

The jeep had pulled up but the singing went on. It was the Old Hundredth, 'Praise God from whom all blessings flow'. Mboga played the last few notes and leapt from the back of the jeep.

"She's brought back and bought back, Bwana!"

We went across. I greeted the girl in her own language. She looked utterly different with those colourful clothes around her head and shoulders.

The whole conversation was translated for Bill's benefit. "He says you are bought back, Mzito, but don't think you have changed ownership; you are free! Mboga paid the money, yes, but . . ."

She pushed the cloth back from her head and nodded, a smile coming over her face.

"Bwana, I understand, but I give myself to him."

"Just because he paid?"

She smiled again. "My thanks for that, Bwana, but my love for just him."

She looked towards Mboga who stood there looking extremely solemn, not quite knowing what to do with his hands.

Simba smiled broadly and Kali chuckled.

"Come on folk, to the hut, I must deal with this tumour tonight."

For the first time since nightfall, Bill smiled.

"What a spoil-sport you are, Doc; there was quite a bit of promise in that situation."

We walked across to the hut.

In one corner was the pressure-lamp with a large mirror

behind it as reflector. The whole room was brilliantly lighted up, and there was comfortable smell of antiseptic.

"Simba, I think the best way to do this job is not to use a table, but this chair. Turn it so that Mzito can put her arms on the back and rest her chin on her arms, like so . . ."

I sat in the appropriate position.

"*Eh-heh*, Bwana."

"Right, we leave the instruments on that box and both that and the chair will be under the mosquito net."

"*Heh*, Bwana, we don't want *dudus* about us when we work."

"Truly, Simba, you can't swat mosquitoes when your hands are scrubbed-up."

The instruments had boiled for the appropriate time and Simba carefully set them out.

Bill put his head round the door with his ever-present camera in his hand.

"Doc, what about a before-and-after shot?"

I asked the African girl about this.

She nodded.

Bill posed her and set off a flash.

Outside, Mboga was keeping himself occupied by playing his *ilimba*.

I lifted my voice. "Mboga, keep handy in case we need anything; play music till I call you."

"Music, Bwana, as much as you like."

Mzito came through the door and I showed her how to sit.

"There will only be small pain, Mzito."

Her hand went to a great welt across her face. "I'm not afraid of pain, Bwana."

She smiled and I nodded.

"First there is medicine that I will inject; you will feel small pricks and the pressure of my fingers and little else."

"Will I not be given sleep medicine, Bwana?"

"*U-huh*, that will not be necessary."

Carefully I swabbed down the tumour.

She raised her head. "Bwana, will you not talk to God before you work?"

"*Eh-heh*, Mzito, we always do that."

Mboga took Bill by the arm and led him into the room.

"We are going to pray, Bill."

I did so in the language the girl understood. We were in the presence of God. I told Him about her tumour and what it had done, and asked for His help in removing it.

Suddenly the girl's voice broke in. "And thank you, O God of all gods, for letting me have this thing, for it brought me to understand." Her voice trailed into silence.

Bill raised his eyes to mine and I nodded.

Softly Mboga's *ilimba* started again. I told Bill the gist of what had been prayed. He looked at me for a moment and then said,

"Say, listen to what Vegetable is playing."

Mboga's skilful thumbs were picking out the tune of 'Count your blessings'.

Again antiseptic was swabbed round the tumour, which itself was enfolded with a bath towel pinned together with safety-pins.

"Am I as you want me, Bwana?" came her voice.

"*Eh-heh*, exactly right, Mzito; we're ready to start now. Hold your arms comfortably and rest your head on them. Ready."

She nodded.

"Just a prick."

She flinched a little.

"Again."

This time she was quiet.

"Again, this is the last one."

"*Yoh*, Bwana, truly it is small pain, nothing worse than the prick of a thorn."

Simba chuckled. "Our ways are somewhat different from the wisdom of witchdoctors, Mzito."

I pinched her skin viciously with a pair of forceps.

"Can you feel anything?" I asked.

She shook her head. "You touched me, Bwana."

Simba grinned.

"Support that thing while I remove it, will you, Simba."

He nodded, and put his large hands beneath the tumour.

Mzito spoke quietly. "I can't feel even the weight of it, Bwana."

"*Eh-heh*, Simba is taking that for you now."

The music of the *ilimba* came on the night air and the girl on whom we were working gently hummed the tune that Mboga played.

There was the subdued snipping of scissors, and then she spoke.

"Bwana, it's gone, I felt it go."

"*Eh-heh*, it's gone all right. And now it is our task to sew you up in such a way that no one will know that you ever had a burden like that."

With forceps, Simba picked up a long curved needle threaded with white cotton. Very carefully the skin was drawn together. Mboga was peering through the mosquito net and watching my activities closely.

"*Heh*, Bwana, for a man you sew with some skill!"

Mzito chuckled.

"When those stitches come out you will see just a very faint line; you will not know that there was anything there before."

Mboga was mumbling inaudibly. Simba listened and pushed a bucket with his foot. The ugly mass we had re-

moved barely fitted into it. Near the doorway Mboga weighed it on a spring balance.

"Fifteen pounds, Bwana."

There were two vivid flashes of light as Bill's camera again came into action.

I was preparing the dressing to put over the stitching when Mboga's voice came.

"Would not Mzito like to see the result of your work, Bwana?"

He was holding two mirrors.

"*Eh-heh*," said the girl, "indeed I would like to see."

The mosquito net was carefully pulled up. I could see Bill getting into position. The girl held one mirror and peered into it and instructed Mboga what to do.

"Move a little to the side. There, stop."

An expression of sheer amazement came over her face as she could see her back clearly. She rolled her eyes.

"*Hongo*, Bwana, it's gone, truly it's *gone*!"

Another flash from Bill's camera. "Boy, what a picture, what an expression! Oh boy!"

The girl took not the slightest notice of any of this but looked toward the door at the unsightly thing in the bucket. She shuddered.

"Oh, Bwana, bury it deep, deep."

"*Hongo*," laughed Mboga, as the last dressing was put into place, "I shall bury that myself, Bwana."

"One more thing to do, Mzito."

I gave an injection of morphia.

"Lie down on the bed over there now and sleep."

CHAPTER XVI

PELICAN LAKE

AT breakfast next morning the Colonel greeted me with, "Well, how's your patient this morning?"

"Up and about, and prepared to set out with Suliman in about an hour's time. She is very well and very happy."

Bill put down his coffee-cup.

"Talking of human interest pictures, those were swell. The look on the girl's face when she saw her back in those mirrors. Oh brother!"

He produced prints. They certainly were fine photography.

"These are for her. She deserves something better—I'll send enlargements later."

Bill then pulled a slip of paper from his pocket.

"I've shot everything that I set out to get. The whole menagerie in action, except those birds, and how I wanted to cover that pelican lake!"

The Colonel smiled. "Don't be too disappointed about that either."

"How come?"

"I rather underestimated Simba. He tells me that he's discovered an alternative path to the place. Nobody is going to be upset if we produce a good counter-attraction at the village."

"Wow! That sounds wonderful. What can we cook up?"

A dismal hyena-howl came from below the camp.

"Odd," said the hunter, "hyenas making a row at this hour."

Bill suddenly got to his feet. "Say, did we ever let that critter out of the trap?"

The Colonel smiled. "I am afraid that in the excitement of the night we forgot that hyena. It spent a sleepless night, I take it!"

"It was not the only one," grunted Bill.

I watched them let down the discomfited creature; it struggled out of the net and disappeared into the jungle at a good round speed, never looking back. Bill grinned all over his face. "That hyena won't go round camps again looking at people in a surly fashion. He's sure learnt his lesson. He's . . . ."

A voice came behind us.

"*Jamba*, Bwana."

An African messenger stood before me with a red-tasselled hat in one hand and a split stick holding a note in the other.

"I have a letter from the chief M'falme, Bwana."

I took it from him and read, "Greetings to you; we are all well at our village. We hope that you too are well. The sick ones with ulcers would have joy to taste your medicine."

I passed the information on.

The Colonel nodded quietly. "Just what we want."

"Suppose, Colonel, we gave them those buck that you shot last night, suggesting that not only should we treat their ulcers, but that we should get the whole village together for a time of beating of drums and of native games and of tasting a little meat."

Bill beamed. "And while everyone is out, Simba leads us to the place where the pelicans put on their own particular dance."

"That's the idea, Bill."

"Swell," he said, "swell."

I wrote a suitably-phrased letter in Swahili and told the messenger that Mboga and I would arrive at M'falme's village at *saa-sita*—noon."

He nodded, saluted and said, "*Kwaheri*—good-bye."

The Colonel was on his feet. "If we are going to make this safari we must make it at once. Dawn is the best time, but in the circumstances we must make the best of what we've got."

There came the sound of Suliman's lorry starting up. We went and said farewell.

I put a note into Mzito's hand, telling Simba's wife, Perisi, exactly what to do for her.

"Two every time you are conscious of the stitches in your back," I smiled, giving her a bottle of aspirin.

"Bwana," she said, looking down, "my heart is full of joy."

"It is a good thing; we will see one another when we return from this safari to the hospital. Stay there with Perisi. Do not leave her house, we do not want your relations to . . ."

She looked at me and smiled. "Bwana, I will follow these words with great care."

Close behind the Indian's lorry went the jeep, the Colonel at the wheel, Bill beside him surrounded by his cameras, Simba and Kali in the back.

"Keep busy, Doc," called Bill's voice as they disappeared in a cloud of dust.

Mboga and I spent quite a time boiling up needles, preparing syringes and all our equipment. We gently put this on the front seat. In the back of the truck there must have been half a ton of buck meat for the feast that we had planned.

Old Tembo the cook sat in a corner surrounded by flies; he grinned as we drove off down the track.

With a mile still to go we could hear the throb of drums and the tongue-trill of African women in their songs of rejoicing.

A horde of people ran out to greet us and trotted beside the car as we came into the village. M'falme was there to greet us with a broad smile on his face.

"*Jambo*, Bwana, we have joy to see you. Truly your medicine is of strength; my pain is gone and the man with ulcers—see . . ."

A grinning individual stood out and held his leg for my inspection. The ulcer was less than half its former size.

In the shade of a mango tree squatted some fifty people; a cloud of flies rose as they stood up.

The chief pointed with his chin. "Many others with ulcers have come."

"*Hongo*, and I have brought much medicine; it is a good thing."

Mboga murmured behind me. "Bwana, the meat, tell him about it now."

"Also, Great One, I have brought a little meat, perhaps it would bring joy to the stomachs of those of your village."

A hundred eager faces pressed closer and Tembo was busy handing out meat for the next ten minutes.

Soon the cooking-pots were bubbling cheerfully over a long fire in a trench.

The *wazereru*—the young men—were done up with red ochre, the blue-bag, and ostrich feathers. They put on a particular turn which was in praise of my medicines and Colonel Johnson's skill in the matter of shooting meat.

The whole village seemed to be there, with the notable exception of the witchdoctor. Mboga had been looking for him too.

"Bwana, he has no joy in today's work. I hear that he sits in his house and thinks thoughts of despondency." He grinned. "Behold, Bwana, the walls of his stomach will remain close together, for he will not join in the feast today."

"Chief," I said, "shall we deal with the sick ones before they eat, or after?"

He smiled. "Bwana, if they eat before, they will be strengthened for small needles."

It was nearly three o'clock when the feast started. Drums had been going incessantly, and there must have been a thousand people crowded round.

I sat with a headman and shared in the meal. The shadows were becoming quite long when the time arrived to treat the ulcers.

I stood them in a long line and made a careful examination. All of them needed the same thing. Penicillin would make an amazing difference in a matter of days.

M'falme stood beside me.

"Great One, cause twelve stools to be brought."

Rapidly he passed on the instruction. They were brought and placed in line. On each a patient was seated.

Carefully I checked over their trouble. Some had ugly long, snake-track ulcers on their arms or legs or faces. Others had punched-out ulcers, again others had swollen, ugly lumps.

As each one was examined I seated him facing the chief's hut. A large syringe was quite full of penicillin. I took the lid off a baking-powder tin which contained a number of very sharp hypodermic needles all carefully threaded through a piece of cloth.

Mboga knew the routine well, and he turned to those who were seated on the stools.

"Move backwards as far as you can and make available for the Bwana that portion of your anatomy where you would have a hip pocket if you wore trousers like the Bwana."

There were grins from those who were not about to be injected.

Mboga had a large swab soaked in iodine. He went along the line, rubbing the appropriate spot, the nearest available portion to the very edge of the stool. Then he and I scrubbed our hands very carefully in two gourds full of water.

"Remember, Mboga, do everything you can with the forceps."

He nodded.

He took out the needles carefully one by one on the end of the forceps. Then with a flourish which made the needle move like the head of a minute spear, it flashed through the skin with a minimum of pain.

"Nice work," I commended. He was as adept with his forehand as his backhand.

I injected penicillin, fitting the syringe to each needle. Mboga followed me and as I finished each injection, he nimbly slipped out the needles and firmly rubbed the spot where they had been.

Each patient set his teeth and said: "*Eeeeh*, it bites."

Four times the stools were occupied. Our routine worked like clockwork.

Soon the clinic was finished. I could see the young men preparing for another dance, but Mboga was before them. His *ilimba* started twanging and he sang a song which brought the people crowding round.

As the people listened, I prayed quietly for wisdom and skill in getting the message of the good news of the Son of God across to these people who were physically sick and as obviously spiritually sick.

My prayer was answered in an unusual way. Mboga suddenly stopped playing.

"Pain brings us no joy?" he asked in a loud voice.

There was a general nodding of heads and a variety of noises indicating the same thing.

"And yet pain is the warning of the body when something is wrong."

He opened his large mouth. "I once had an enemy here." There was a gap between his teeth.

"*Yoh*, the pain of it," he screwed up his face. "I came to the Bwana, he pulled out the tooth, truly it was an evil one,

H

there was an *ipu*—an abscess—beneath it. When the tooth came out, the pain went."

He turned to the chief, who nodded.

"*Eh-heh*, these are words of truth, did it not happen to me the other day?"

He fumbled and produced the stone that had passed down from his kidneys.

"Truly, Great One, pain was the warning of your body, but you don't feel pain in your soul, you feel fear. Let there be no mistake, fear is the pain of the soul. Sin causes that fear. The only One who can take it away is Jesus Christ, the Son of God. His words are here."

I held out a Bible.

"Are there those who can read here?"

Tadayo stood forward. "Bwana, I can; also I shall explain the words of the Book, if the chief agrees."

"*Eheeh!*" nodded M'falme, "Tadayo may stay and read us the words."

"This is a wise way, Great One, for in that Book is the medicine for the soul as in the syringe was medicine for your bodies."

The sun had set when we waved good-bye to what was now a very friendly village.

Back at the camp I met an enthusiastic Bill. He was carefully storing films in tins and sealing and labelling them.

He looked up. "Oh, brother, what a show! *Pelicans*, I'll say I saw pelicans, right up close, oh it was a wonderful spot —you should have seen it. You should have seen them dance! Clumsy critters they may be on land but in the water they move like ballet dancers.

"I shot five hundred feet of it and would have taken a thousand more, too, if the Colonel hadn't shot a crocodile and disturbed the whole show."

A smile came over Colonel Johnson's face. "You didn't mention that the crocodile was only six feet away and taking a lively interest in you."

Bill shrugged, supremely uninterested in crocodiles. "And Doc, the sky was alive with hundreds of thousands of birds, especially flamingos."

Bill rolled his eyes. "The shots I got of pink birds against blue sky . . ." He shook his head. "I've never photographed anything in colour like it."

"How did you go, Doctor?" asked the Colonel.

"Quite a neat little diversion, thanks. Useful in many ways."

Later on that evening round the camp-fire the hunter took me aside.

"I don't think Bailey is as well as he might be. The unusual nature of today's happenings lifted him for the time being, but I expect him to be pretty down tomorrow."

CHAPTER XVII

THE TRYPNASOME

NEXT morning Bill Bailey sat on the side of his bed, his head in his hands. Mboga brought him a cup of coffee. He drank some and made a face.

"Doc, my mouth's lined with fur today and my head . . ."

"Too many pelicans," I laughed.

Bill looked up. "It wasn't pelicans last night, it was lions. I dreamt about 'em. You know, Doc, I have photographed lions large and small, male and female, till I can see them without looking.

"A month ago, if anyone had told me that a lion would yawn at me and I'd yawn back, I'd have regarded him as bats, but the lions hereabout are so used to photographers from Arizona that . . ."

"Ah, you need some vitamin pills, Bill."

He grinned. "Maybe, but boy, oh boy, I'm tired."

He rolled back into his camp-bed.

Half an hour later I came back with equipment to take a blood slide. He was sitting in his tent, an open photographic journal before him, but his eyes stared straight through the table.

"Your finger, Bill."

Silently he pushed his hand across. I collected the necessary drip of blood and walked across to the microscope set up on a packing-case under a thornbush.

Without comment Colonel Johnson came and sat down near me.

On the piece of glass was a smear of blood the size of a thumbprint. I stained and prepared it and put it under the lens, slowly moving it to and fro.

There were red blood-cells by the thousand, looking like tiny peach petals. Amongst them, stained deep purple, were the white blood-cells. Systematically the whole smear was examined. The blood cells seemed unending until suddenly there came into view the parasite that causes sleeping-sickness.

I whistled quietly through my teeth.

"Trypnasomes, Colonel!"

His lips hardly moved as he spoke very softly. "Many of them, Doctor?"

Still looking down the eyepiece I said, "Yes, it's a severe infection."

"You're not happy about him?"

"Not exactly. I've everything that is usually needed in the way of medicines, but he's allergic in his reaction to a lot of things and arsenic is hostile stuff. The only safe thing to do is to give a small trial dose and if that goes smoothly all's well, but if not . . ."

"I understand; it's get him out quickly to hospital."

"Just that. First, though, he must have a full picture of what is happening."

I went across to where my patient was sitting, his face covered with a moist towel.

"Doc," he groaned, "this is the father and mother of all headaches."

I ran my hand behind his head. There, sure enough, behind the ears were large lymph glands.

He looked up at me, a question in his half-closed eyes.

"You've picked up sleeping-sickness, Bill."

His lips framed for a whistle. "Can you do anything about it, Doc?"

"Sure, look."

Into his hand I put a glass ampoule with a formidable chemical name on it.

"You need a shot of this stuff, it's a special form of arsenic."

"Arsenic . . .?" His eyebrows went up and an odd smile twisted the corners of his mouth. "Trying to poison the poor photographer, eh?"

"Not exactly," I grinned back, "the idea is to poison the *dudus* with a dose of this that isn't strong enough to kill the average patient."

"That's swell," came back his drawl, "but am I an average patient?"

"That's exactly what I'm going to find out. I don't trust you, Bill, you and your allergy. You puff up like a balloon if you eat cheese, come out in red spots if you swallow iron pills, and sneeze twenty times in succession if you come anywhere near certain sorts of grass. That being so, what's going to happen to you if you're injected with arsenic?"

Bill shrugged his shoulders. "If arsenic's what I need, let's go."

I mixed a minute quantity of the anti-sleeping-sickness medicine in saline solution and drew it up into a syringe. To be on the safe side I filled another from a rubber-capped bottle labelled 'Adrenalin.'

An odd sixth sense within me was flashing on red lights and ringing warning bells as I stretched Bill's arm on the table, palm upwards, and swabbed the elbow.

"Open and close your fingers a bit."

He did so. I slipped the needle into a vein and injected.

He grinned up at me. "Why, Doc, there is nothing to it, say this does nothing to me, it . . . oh—oh!"

Even as he spoke a wary look came into his eyes. There was a pause, then he said, "My tongue is getting heavy, my lips are swelling."

His face started to puff up, his eyes seemed to disappear, his lips became thicker than Mboga's, his voice went husky and he started to scratch as his skin became intensely red.

The second syringe held three times the ordinary dose of adrenalin. Slowly I injected this and followed it with morphia.

The big-game hunter was standing outside the tent; he turned questioningly.

"Colonel, this is a matter of urgency. He's proved highly sensitive to the only effective remedy on hand, the only anti-sleeping-sickness drug that's available in East Africa."

He nodded and said crisply. "What's the next step?"

"Hospital, either in Nairobi, or New York. The latter, I think."

Colonel Johnson nodded again.

"We can charter a plane to get him to Nairobi, pick up the afternoon aircraft . . ."

"Yes, I see the picture. I'll drive to a place where I can make a radio contact with Arusha and charter the plane. Leave it to me."

He sat behind the wheel of the jeep and I watched a long ribbon of dust slowly move over the plain as he drove due north.

In the tent Mboga was keeping the hot air moving with a moist towel. Bill lay quietly, the swelling of his face was gradually settling down. His lips moved. I caught the word 'water'.

He sipped some and spoke huskily. "What's cooking, Doc?"

"There's only one thing for it Bill; we'll have to get you to hospital."

"Is it urgent? Does every hour count?"

"No, it's not as bad as that, but the sooner treatment is started the better."

He nodded. "Doc, if I'm going to hospital, I'm going to hospital in New York."

"That's what we thought; the Colonel has arrangements in hand. It seems fantastic that it took David Livingstone six months to get from Glasgow to the Cape of Good Hope. Now we can land you in New York in thirty-six hours.

"We are chartering a plane in Nairobi that can land on the strip near here—the pilot has done it before—and he ought to be here by a little after dawn. This should fix things for you to catch an early afternoon plane, change at Rome and land in New York pretty smartly."

"Do that, Doc," came the voice, "that's swell."

He sipped some more water and his voice came less huskily. "It was bad, Doc, seeing Ibrahim torn by the leopard, but you're sure right, the teeth of the tsetse fly do more damage than any leopard's teeth or claws."

And then quietly, "And I've gotten that disease, sleeping-sickness."

"That's the situation, and the uncomfortable fact is that the one available effective drug can't be used, you're sensitive to it."

Bill nodded. "Sleeping-sickness, eh? Then what you're saying is, that you can fly me up to New York, and in a couple of days or less, they'll fill me up with some rare medicine which will cope with tsetse-fly bites and all the trimmings."

I nodded.

He lay back on his pillow. "What I can't get out of my mind is the thousands of people out here in Tanganyika who haven't got a hospital to go to, or the medicines to be squirted into their veins."

"It helps you to understand why I'm a medical missionary."

He put his hand to his head. "Oh, brother, and I used to think that missions were a waste of time. Sure, I've learned a lot out here, watching guys like Simba and Mboga and that girl Mzito."

He took another drink. "When I came out here, Doc, to Africa, I was like that girl, I had a burden on my back, but it's gone now."

He groped for the small Testament which I had given him.

"I asked Him to cope with it, like the girl asked you to remove the thing from her back. He did for me what you did for her, but it was a bigger operation."

I nodded. "Yes, Bill, you're right, and it's He, not you who carries the scar."

He seemed to fall asleep.

I tiptoed out to write to an American doctor, famous for his work in tropical medicine.

Bill's eyes opened and he grinned at Mboga. "Keep flapping that towel, Vegetable," he said.

I went on writing.

A half-snore came from the camp-bed.

Mboga's eyes twinkled and he whispered:

"Truly, he sleeps now, Bwana."

In the early afternoon Kali ran over to me.

"*Kule!* Right over there, Bwana."

A ribbon of dust in the distance heralded the return of the jeep. I went across to meet it.

The Colonel stepped briskly out of the sturdy little vehicle.

"Everything is arranged, Doctor. They'll fly in a little Auster not long after dawn. We had better get to work now and pack all his gear. How's Bailey now?"

"Sound asleep and reasonably comfortable."

It was dusk by the time we had finished. Mboga had lighted the camp-fire; Tembo was cooking something that smelt most appetizing.

From Bill's tent came the creak of a camp-bed. I went in. He yawned and sat up in bed looking very much himself again.

"Time for a little something, eh Doc?" he said, wriggling his nose.

He did justice to gazelle steak, and then turned to me.

"Say, Doc, what about a game of chess?"

I set up the game by the light of the hurricane lamp. The camp-fire lit up the area; the limbs of the small trees showed from time to time and the stars shone brilliantly above them.

We played for a while. The Africans were sitting on the far side of the fire. Suddenly we heard:

"*Punghati!*"

Bill took my rook and smiled. "Old Simba has a special signature spit all right!"

We played on again for a while. Far out an elephant trumpeted, the crickets chirped and there was the faint rhythm of distant drums.

Simba and Mboga were sitting on the running-board of the three-tonner, their heads bowed.

Bill pointed across to them. "What do you think they're doing, Doc?"

"They're praying, Joe, for Mzito and Perisi and the hospital and for you and me."

He nodded and rolled a pawn round in his fingers.

"Have you ever felt death in your veins, Doc?"

"Twice; it's not very comfortable, is it? It's not very terrifying either if . . ."

Bill nodded and winced as he did so. "You're going to say, if you've got no burden on your back, eh?"

I agreed.

"On our money in the States is written 'In God we trust'. That was only words to me till these days."

The game turned in my favour suddenly; gleefully I snapped up Bill's Queen. He didn't notice—he was staring far out into the jungle.

"What about some coffee, Bill? You must get some sleep tonight; you've a long safari at dawn."

"Coffee would be swell."

As I poured it out, I put a pill into his hand. He nodded and swallowed it.

Dawn was ushered in by enthusiastic birds. There was a chill in the early morning breeze as all Joe's equipment was carefully carried to the flat strip of grass where the plane would land.

We marked out the area carefully with sheets, and then walked six abreast to clear away sticks and stones and thorn-bush.

Breakfast was nearly over when Simba pointed with his chin to a faint speck coming in towards us from the north-west. Rapidly it grew bigger and soon circled over us and came in to land.

We walked over to the plane together and the pilot came across and shook hands.

"Where's the patient?" he asked.

"Say, I'm the patient," said Bill.

The airman raised his eyebrows. "You don't look too bad."

"I'm aiming to stay that way," replied Bill.

He watched all his precious material being stowed away, then he turned round to us all.

"Colonel, it's been a wonderful safari."

I handed him a letter. "The moment you get to the New York airport, ring this doctor, give him this letter and get on with the treatment. Let's know at the first possible moment how things go."

"I sure will."

He gripped my hand. "Doc, it's been good to make this journey. Thanks for all your medicines and par-ticularly . . ."

His voice grew quiet. "For introducing me to the biggest medicine of the lot."

With his thumb he pushed up my New Testament which now reposed in his shirt pocket.

"I won't forget anything that I learned on this safari."

He got into the plane and waved, " Kwaheri—good-bye!"

The plane taxied and took off lightly and disappeared the way it had come.

It didn't take us long to strike camp. When we were loaded, the Colonel came over to me.

"Well, Doctor, I'm going on up to Arusha. Would you mind taking the three-tonner back to Dodoma?"

"Certainly, Colonel. It's been a good safari, I have en-joyed almost every minute of it."

My mind went back to the half-light of an evening, when I saw a figure terrified, staring into the cold eyes of a leopard.

Then again I experienced the moment of shock of seeing sleeping-sickness parasites in Bill's blood-slide.

Apparently the Colonel had been thinking much the same way. He gripped my hand and handed me an envelope.

"There's a cheque in there. It should run your hospital for quite a while."

I thanked him, and again we said good-bye.

*   *   *   *

A month later, after a happy and useful visit to the hospital in the big-game country, I found myself back again at our Jungle Hospital. With pleasurable anticipation of a good medical result, I took the final dressing from Mzito's back. Mboga was looking on.

The wound had completely healed; there was only a faint scar. Without more ado, we turned to the discussion of wedding arrangements!

From outside the window came a tired voice. "*Hodi*— may I come in?"

"*Karibu*—come in."

"Bwana, *simu*—cable."

I tore open the envelope; the words on the yellow paper read:

"DUDUS DOING NICELY STOP TRIUMPH OVER TSE AND TRYPNASOME NOW CERTAIN STOP TELL MZITO MY BURDEN ALSO GONE FOR GOOD STOP MBOGA KNEW HIS ONIONS REGARD SPINACH AS FIRST-CLASS VEGETABLE STOP CHARGE WEDDING FEAST TO MRS. BAILEY'S ONLY SON STOP WE CERTAINLY HUNTED BIG GAME."